# Foundations of Chemistry in the Laboratory

**HEIN • PEISEN • BEST • MINER**

## CHE 100

**General Chemistry**
**Chemistry Department**
**Ammerman Campus**
**Suffolk County Community College**

—— **Wiley Custom Learning Solutions** ——

# FOUNDATIONS OF CHEMISTRY IN THE LABORATORY

## TWELFTH EDITION

**Morris Hein**
*Mount San Antonio College*

**Judith N. Peisen**
*Hagerstown Community College*

**Leo R. Best**
*Mount San Antonio College*

**Robert L. Miner**
*Mount San Antonio College*

John Wiley & Sons, Inc.

Cover Photo: Digital Vision/Getty Images

To order books or for customer service call 1-800-CALL-WILEY (225-5945).

ISBN-13    978-0-470-04385-1

ISBN-10    0-470-04385-7

Printed in the United States of America

Printed and bound by Bind-Rite Graphics.

# Contents

**EXPERIMENTS**

**STUDY AIDS**

**EXERCISES**

## APPENDICES

# To the Student

Since your laboratory time is limited, it is important to come to each session prepared by at least one hour of detailed study of the scheduled experiment. This should be considered a standing homework assignment.

Each of the experiments in this manual is composed of four parts:

1. **Materials, Equipment, and Chemicals Safety**—a list of what you need to perform the experiment that includes the formulas of all substances used (except for unknowns).

2. **Discussion**—a brief discussion of the principles underlying the experiment.

3. **Procedure**—detailed directions for performing the experiment with safety precautions clearly noted and disposal procedures for chemical waste provided throughout and identified by a waste icon.

4. **Report for Experiment**—a form for recording data and observations, performing calculations, and answering questions.

Follow the directions in the procedure carefully, and consult your instructor if you have any questions. For convenience, the letters and subtitles in the report form have been set up to correspond with those in the procedure section of each experiment.

As you make your observations and obtain your data, record them on the report form. Try to use your time efficiently; when a reaction or process is occurring that takes considerable time and requires little watching, start working on other parts of the experiment, perform calculations, answer questions on the report form, or clean up your equipment.

Except when your instructor directs otherwise, you should do all the work individually. You may profit by discussing experimental results with your classmates, but in the final analysis you must rely on your own judgment in completing the report form.

## ⚠ Safety Guidelines

In the chemistry laboratory, you are responsible not only for your own safety but for the safety of everyone else. *We have included safety precautions in every experiment where needed, and they are highlighted with the icon shown in the title of this section.* Your instructor may modify these instructions and give you more specific directions on safety in your laboratory. If the proper precautions and techniques are used, none of the experiments in this laboratory program are hazardous. But without your reading and following the instructions, without knowledge about handling and disposal of chemicals, and without the use of common sense at all times, accidents can happen. Even when everyone is doing his or her best to comply with the safety guidelines in each experiment, accidents can happen. It is your responsibility to minimize these accidents and know what to do if they happen.

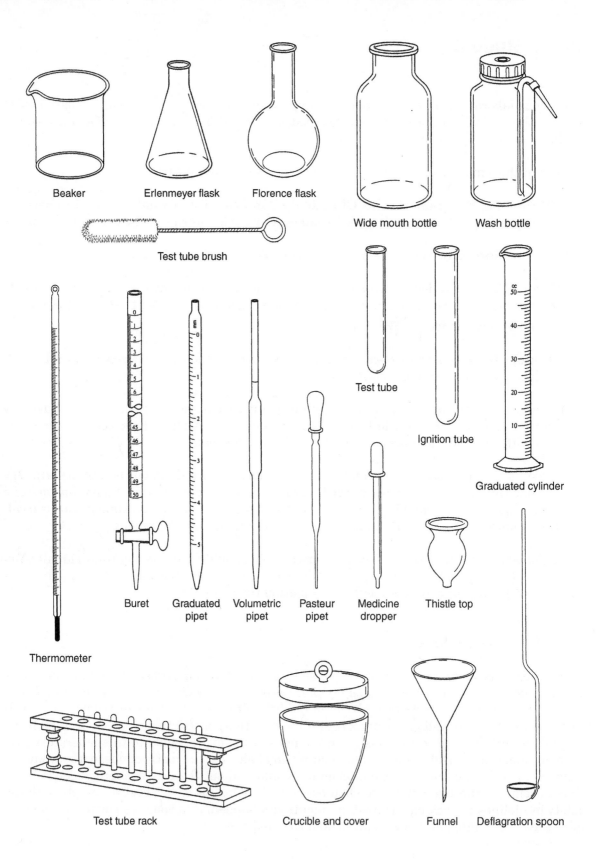

Beaker

Erlenmeyer flask

Florence flask

Wide mouth bottle

Wash bottle

Test tube brush

Test tube

Ignition tube

Graduated cylinder

Thermometer

Buret

Graduated pipet

Volumetric pipet

Pasteur pipet

Medicine dropper

Thistle top

Test tube rack

Crucible and cover

Funnel

Deflagration spoon

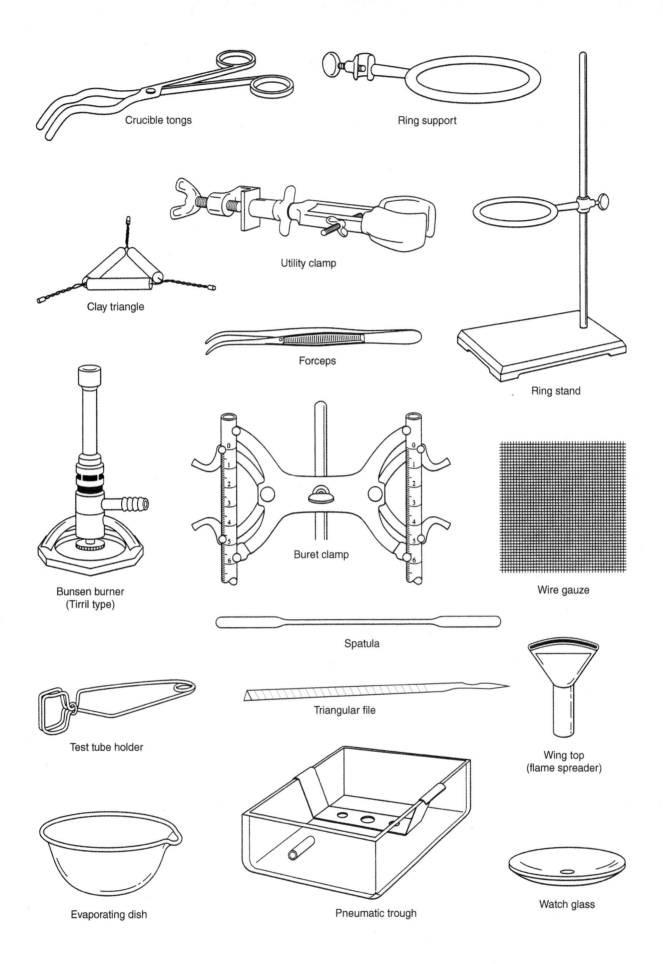

Crucible tongs

Ring support

Utility clamp

Clay triangle

Forceps

Ring stand

Bunsen burner
(Tirril type)

Buret clamp

Wire gauze

Spatula

Test tube holder

Triangular file

Wing top
(flame spreader)

Evaporating dish

Pneumatic trough

Watch glass

# LABORATORY TECHNIQUES

## A.  Laboratory Burners

Almost all laboratory burners used today are modifications of a design by the German chemist Robert Bunsen. In Bunsen's fundamental design, also widely used in domestic and industrial gas burners, gas and air are premixed by admitting the gas at relatively high velocity from a jet in the base of the burner. This rapidly moving stream of gas causes air to be drawn into the barrel from side ports and to mix with the gas before entering the combustion zone at the top of the burner.

The burner is connected to a gas cock by a short length of rubber or plastic tubing. With some burners the gas cock is turned to the **fully on** position when the burner is in use, and the amount of gas admitted to the burner is controlled by adjusting a needle valve in the base of the burner. In burners that do not have this needle valve, the gas flow is regulated by partly opening or closing the gas cock. With either type of burner the gas should **always be turned off at the gas cock** (Figure 0.0) when the burner is not in use (to avoid possible dangerous gas leakage from the needle valve or old tubing).

**Figure 0.0    Both levers are in the off position.**

**Operating the Burner.**  Examine the construction of your burner (Figure 0.1) and familiarize yourself with its operation. A burner is usually lighted with the air inlet ports nearly closed. The ports are closed by rotating the barrel of the burner in a clockwise direction. After the gas has been turned on and lighted, the size and quality of the flame is adjusted by admitting air and regulating the flow of gas. Air is admitted by rotating the barrel; gas is regulated with the needle valve, if present, or the gas cock. Insufficient air will cause a luminous yellow, smoky flame; too much air will cause the flame to be noisy and possibly blow out. A Bunsen burner flame that is satisfactory for most purposes is shown in Figure 0.2; such a flame is said to be "nonluminous." Note that the hottest region is immediately above the bright blue cone of a well-adjusted flame.

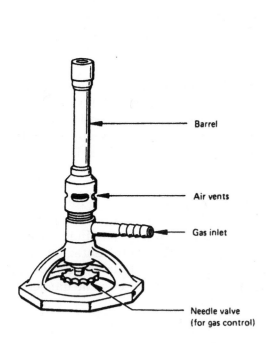

Figure 0.1   Bunsen burner (Tirrill type)

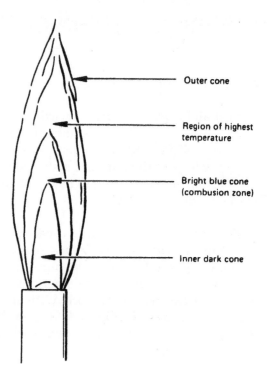

Outer cone

Region of highest temperature

Bright blue cone (combusion zone)

Inner dark cone

Figure 0.2   Bunsen burner flame

## B.   Evaporation

Evaporation is one of the processes used to separate a dissolved solid from a liquid.

1. Obtain a Bunsen burner, small ring clamp, large ring clamp, wire gauze, and clay triangle.  Attach the small ring clamp to the ring stand so that it is about 2 to 3 inches above the top of the Bunsen burner.  Place the wire gauze and beaker on it.  Clamp the large ring to the ring stand so that it is near the middle of the beaker (Figure 0.3).

Light the burner and check to see that the hottest part of the flame is just below the wire gauze, if it is not make the necessary adjustments.  Move the burner away from the ring stand.  Fill the beaker about 2/3 full with tap water, place it on the ceramic wire gauze.

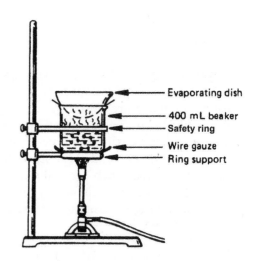

Evaporating dish

400 mL beaker
Safety ring

Wire gauze
Ring support

Figure 0.3   Evaporation on a simple water bath

2. **Evaporating the Solution.**  Pour the solution  into an evaporating dish. Place the evaporating dish on the beaker of water being heated. Light the burner and place it under the beaker. Continue heating the water to maintain boiling—add more water to the beaker as needed—until all of the water has evaporated from the solution in the evaporating dish, leaving the solid as the residue. Use crucible tongs to remove the evaporating dish from the beaker. Use beaker tongs to remove the beaker of hot water from the ring stand.  Pour the hot water into your sink.

## C.  Filtration

The process of separating suspended insoluble solids from liquids by means of filters is called **filtration**. Insoluble solids, called **precipitates**, are formed during some chemical reactions. In the laboratory these precipitates are generally separated from the solutions by filtering them out on a paper filter. The liquid that passes through the filter paper is the **filtrate**; the solid precipitate remaining on the filter paper is the **residue**.

### Filtering the Products.

a.  Fold a circle of filter paper in half. Fold in half again and open out into a cone.

b.  Fit the opened cone into a short-stemmed funnel. Wet with distilled water and press the top edge of the paper against the funnel, forming a seal.

c.  Use the setup in Figure 0.4 for supporting the funnel.

d.  Stir the mixture of products in the small beaker with a stirring rod and slowly pour it down the stirring rod into the filter paper in the funnel (see Figure 0.5).

e.  Do not overfill the paper filter cone.

f.  Use forceps to remove the filter paper with the precipitate and transfer it into the waste jar provided. Pour the filtrate into the waste bottle provided. Rinse the reaction beaker and the test tubes with water and pour the rinse solutions into the waste bottle.

Review the safety procedures for chemical waste disposal in the preface to determine the specific reasons for putting the waste into special containers rather than the trash and the sink.

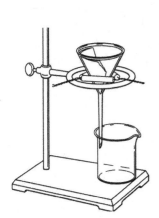

**Figure 0.4    Support the filter with a ring stand or an Erlenmeyer flask**

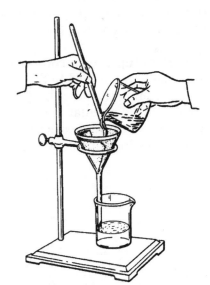

**Figure 0.5    Pouring a solution down a stirring rod**

# D. Use of a Buret

## Use of the Buret

A buret is a volumetric instrument that is calibrated to deliver a measured volume of solution. The 50 mL buret is calibrated from 0 to 50 mL in 0.1 mL increments and is read to the nearest 0.01 mL. All volumes delivered from the buret should be between the calibration marks. (Do not estimate above the 0 mL mark or below the 50 mL mark.)

1. **Cleaning the Buret.**   The buret must be clean in order to deliver the calibrated volume. Drops of liquid clinging to the sides as the buret is drained are evidence of a dirty buret.

To clean the buret, first rinse it a couple of times with tap water, pouring the water from a beaker. Then scrub it with a detergent solution, using a long-handled buret brush. Rinse the buret several times with tap water and finally with distilled water. Check for cleanliness by draining the distilled water through the tip and observe whether droplets of water remain on the inner walls of the buret.

2. **Using the Buret.**   After draining the distilled water, rinse the buret with two 5 to 10 mL portions of the titrating solution to be used in it. This rinsing is done by holding the buret in a horizontal position and rolling the solution around to wet the entire inner surface. Allow the final rinsing to drain through the tip.

Fill the buret with the solution to slightly above the 0 mL mark and adjust it to 0.00 mL, or some other volume below this mark, by draining the solution through the tip. The buret tip must be completely filled to deliver the volume measured.

To deliver the solution from the buret, turn the stopcock with the forefinger and the thumb of your left hand (if you are right handed) to allow the solution to enter the flask. (See Figure 0.6). This procedure leaves your right hand free to swirl the solution in the flask during the titration. With a little practice you can control the flow so that increments as small as 1 drop of solution can be delivered.

3. **Reading the Buret.**   The smallest calibration mark of a 50 mL buret is 0.1 mL. However, the buret is read to the nearest 0.01 mL by estimating between the calibration marks. When reading the buret be sure your line of sight is level with the bottom of the meniscus in order to avoid parallax errors (see Figure 0.7). The exact bottom of the meniscus may be made more prominent and easier to read by allowing the meniscus to pick up the reflection from a heavy dark line on a piece of paper (see Figure 0.8).

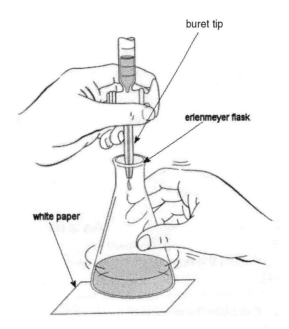

**Figure 0.6    Titration technique**

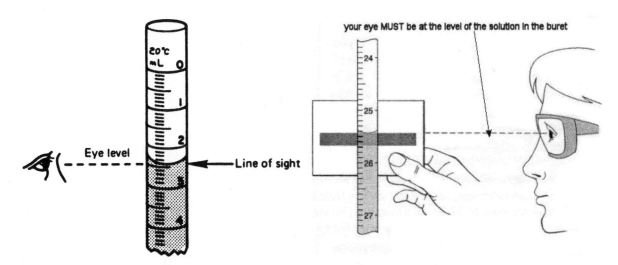

**Figure 0.7    Reading the buret. The line of sight must be level with the bottom of the meniscus to avoid parallax.**

**Figure 0.8    Reading the meniscus. A heavy dark line brought to within one division of the meniscus will make the meniscus more prominent and easier to read. The volume reading is 25.42 mL.**

# EXPERIMENT 1

## The Periodic Table

Name: _____

Date: _____

Fill in the blanks with the symbol of the elements based on the periodic table you built. Leave boxes blank where appropriate.

# EXPERIMENT 2

## Measurements

**MATERIALS**

Ice, ruler, thermometer, solid object, solid rubber stopper, ring stand, ceramic wire gauze, small ring clamp, large ring clamp, beaker tongs, beakers (100, 150, 250, 400-mL), graduated cylinders (10, 50-mL), 125-mL Erlenmeyer flask, test tubes

**EQUIPMENT**

Balance (0.01g)

**CHEMICALS**

**SAFETY**

Chemical splash goggles and lab coat

**DISCUSSION**

Chemistry is an experimental science, and measurements are fundamental to most of the experiments. It is important to learn how to make and use these measurements properly.

**The SI System of Units**

The International System of Units (*Systeme Internationale, SI*) or metric system is a decimal system of units for measurements used almost exclusively in science. It is built around a set of units including the meter, the gram, and the liter and uses factors of 10 to express larger or smaller multiples of these units. To express larger or smaller units, prefixes are added to the names of the units. Deci, centi, and milli are units that are 1/10, 1/100, and 1/1000, respectively, of these units. The most common of these prefixes with their corresponding values expressed as decimals and powers of 10 are shown in the table below.

| Prefix | Decimal Equivalent | Power of 10 | Examples |
|--------|--------------------|-------------|----------|
| deci (d) | 0.1 | $10^{-1}$ | $1\ dg = 0.1\ g = 10^{-1}\ g$ |
| centi (c) | 0.01 | $10^{-2}$ | $1\ cm = 0.01\ m = 10^{-2}\ m$ |
| milli (m) | 0.001 | $10^{-3}$ | $1\ mg = 0.001\ g = 10^{-3}\ g$ |
| kilo (k) | 1000 | $10^{3}$ | $1\ km = 1000\ m = 10^{3}\ m$ |

## Dimensional Analysis

It will often be necessary to convert from the American System of units to the SI system or to convert units within the SI system. Conversion factors are available from tables (see Appendix 1) or can be developed from the metric prefixes and their corresponding values as shown in the table above. Dimensional analysis, a problem-solving method with many applications in chemistry, is very valuable for converting one unit to another by the use of conversion factors. A review of using dimensional analysis for converting units is provided here. Study Aid 4 provides more help with this problem-solving tool.

Conversion Factors come from equivalent relationships, usually stated as equations. From each equivalence statement two conversion factors can be written in fractional form with a value of 1. For example:

| Equivalence Equations | Conversion Factor #1 | Conversion Factor #2 |
| --- | --- | --- |
| 1 dollar = 4 quarters | $\dfrac{1 \text{ dollar}}{4 \text{ quarters}}$ | $\dfrac{4 \text{ quarters}}{1 \text{ dollar}}$ |
| 1 lb = 453.6 g | $\dfrac{1 \text{ lb}}{453.6 \text{ g}}$ | $\dfrac{453.6 \text{ g}}{1 \text{ lb}}$ |
| 1 mm = $10^{-3}$ m | $\dfrac{1 \text{ mm}}{10^{-3} \text{ m}}$ | $\dfrac{10^{-3} \text{ m}}{1 \text{ mm}}$ |
| 1 ns = $10^{-9}$ s | $\dfrac{1 \text{ ns}}{10^{-9} \text{ s}}$ | $\dfrac{10^{-9} \text{ s}}{1 \text{ ns}}$ |

The dimensional analysis method of converting units involves organizing one or more conversion factors into a logical series which cancels or eliminates all units except the unit(s) wanted in the answer.

For example:  To convert 2.53 lb into milligrams (mg), the setup is:

$$(2.53 \text{ lb})\left(\frac{453.6 \text{ g}}{1 \text{ lb}}\right)\left(\frac{1 \text{ mg}}{10^{-3} \text{ g}}\right) = 1.15 \times 10^6 \text{ mg}$$

Note, that in completing this calculation, units are treated as numbers, lb in the denominator is canceled into lb in the numerator and g in the denominator is cancelled into g in the numerator. More examples of unit conversions can be found in Study Aid 4.

Although the SI unit of temperature is the Kelvin (K), the Celsius (or centigrade) temperature scale is commonly used in scientific work and the Fahrenheit scale is commonly used in this country. On the Celsius scale the freezing point of water is designated 0°C, the boiling point 100°C.

## Precision and Accuracy of Measurements

Scientific measurements must be as **precise and accurate** as possible. This means that every measurement will include one uncertain or estimated digit. When making measurements we normally estimate between the smallest scale divisions on the instrument being used. Then, only the uncertain digit should vary if the measurement is repeated using the same instrument, even if it is repeated by someone else. The **accuracy** of a measurement or calculated quantity refers to its agreement with some known value. For example, we need to make two measurements, volume and mass, to determine the density of a metal. This experimental density can then be compared with the density of the metal listed in a reference such as the *Handbook of Chemistry and Physics*. High accuracy means there is good agreement between the experimental value and the known value listed in the reference. Not all measurements can be compared with a known value.

### Precision and Significant Figures

When a measured value is determined to the highest precision of the measuring instrument, the digits in the measurement are called **significant digits** or **significant figures.**

Suppose we are measuring two pieces of wire, using the metric scale on a ruler that is calibrated in tenths of centimeters as shown in Figures 2.1a and b. One end of the first wire is placed at exactly 0.0 cm and the other end falls somewhere between 6.3 cm and 6.4 cm. Since the distance between 6.3 and 6.4 is very small, it is difficult to determine the next digit exactly. One person might estimate the length of the wire as 6.34 cm and another as 6.33 cm. The estimated digit is never ignored because it tells us that the ruler can be read to the 0.01 place. This measurement therefore has three significant figures (two certain and one uncertain figure).

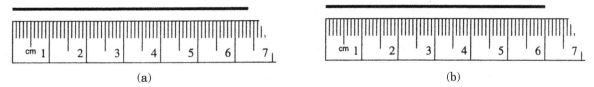

(a)                                                          (b)

**Figure 2.1**

The second wire has a length which measures exactly 6 cm on the ruler as shown in Figure 2.1b. Reporting this length as 6 cm would be a mistake for it would imply that the 6 is an uncertain digit and others might record 5 or 7 as the measurement. Recording the measurement as 6.0 would also be incorrect because it implies that the 0 is uncertain and that someone else might estimate the length as 6.1 or 5.9. What we really mean is that, as closely as we can read it, the length is exactly 6 cm. So, we must write the number in such a way that it tells how precisely we can read it. In this example we can estimate to 0.01 cm so the length should be reported as 6.00 cm.

### Significant Figures in Calculations

The result of multiplication, division, or other mathematical manipulation cannot be more precise than the least precise measurement used in the calculation. For instance, suppose we have an object that weighs 3.62 lb and we want to calculate the mass in grams. $(3.62\,\text{lb})\left(\dfrac{453.6\,\text{g}}{1\,\text{lb}}\right)$ = 1,642.032 when done by a calculator. To report 1,642.032 g as the mass is absurd, for it implies a precision far beyond that of the original measurement. Although the conversion factor has four significant figures, the mass in pounds has only three significant figures. Therefore the answer should have only three significant figures; that is, 1,640 g. In this case the zero cannot be considered significant. This value can be more properly expressed as $1.64 \times 10^3$ g. For a more comprehensive discussion of significant figures see Study Aid 1.

## Precise Quantities versus Approximate Quantities

In conducting an experiment it is often unnecessary to measure an exact quantity of material. For instance, the directions might state, "Weigh about 2 g of sodium sulfite." This instruction indicates that the measured quantity of salt should be 2 g plus or minus a small quantity. In this example 1.8 to 2.2 g will satisfy these requirements. To weigh exactly 2.00 g or 2.000 g wastes time since the directions call for approximately 2 g.

Sometimes it is necessary to measure an amount of material precisely within a stated quantity range. Suppose the directions read, "weigh about 2 g of sodium sulfite to the nearest 0.001 g." This instruction does not imply that the amount is 2.000 g but that it should be between 1.8 and 2.2 g and measured and recorded to three decimal places. Therefore, four different students might weigh their samples and obtain 2.141 g, 2.034 g, 1.812 g, and 1.937 g, respectively, and each would have satisfactorily followed the directions.

## Temperature

The simple act of measuring a temperature with a thermometer can easily involve errors. Not only does the calibration of the scale on the thermometer limit the precision of the measurement, but the improper placement of the thermometer bulb in the material being measured introduces a common source of human error. When measuring the temperature of a liquid, one can minimize this type of error by observing the following procedures:

1. Hold the thermometer away from the walls of the container.

2. Allow sufficient time for the thermometer to reach equilibrium with the liquid.

3. Be sure the liquid is adequately mixed.

When converting from degrees Celsius to Fahrenheit or vice versa, we make use of the following formulas:

$$°C = \frac{(°F - 32)}{1.8} \quad \text{or} \quad °F = (1.8 \times °C) + 32$$

**Example Problem:** Convert 70.0°F to degrees Celsius:

$$°C = \left(\frac{70.0°F - 32}{1.8}\right) = \frac{38.0}{1.8} = 21.11°C \text{ rounded to } 21.1°C$$

This example shows not only how the formula is used but also a typical setup of the way chemistry problems should be written. It shows how the numbers are used, but does not show the multiplication and division, which should be worked out by calculator. The answer was changed from 21.11°C to 21.1°C because the initial temperature, 70.0°F, has only three significant figures. The 1.8 and 32 in the formulas are exact numbers and have no effect on the number of significant figures.

## Mass (Weight)

The directions in this manual are written for a 0.001 gram precision balance, but all the experiments can be performed satisfactorily using a 0.01 gram or 0.0001 gram precision balance.

Your instructor will give specific directions on how to use the balance, but the following precautions should be observed:

1. The balance should always be "zeroed" before anything is placed on the balance pan. On an electronic digital balance, this is done with the "tare" or "T" button. Balances without this feature should be adjusted by the instructor.

2. Never place chemicals directly on the balance pan; first place them on a weighing paper, weighing "boat", or in a container. Clean up any materials you spill on or around the balance.

3. For the analytical (0.0001 g) balance:

   a.  Make sure that all of the doors are closed,

   b.  That the object is at the temperature of the balance room,

   c.  That the object is dry.

4. Never try to make adjustments on a balance. If it seems out of order, tell your instructor.

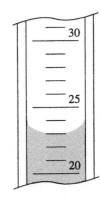

## Volume

Beakers and flasks are marked to indicate only approximate volumes. Volume measurements are therefore made in a graduated cylinder by reading the point on the graduated scale that coincides with the bottom of the curved surface called the **meniscus** of the liquid (Figure 2.2). Volumes measured in this illustrated graduated cylinder are calibrated in 1 mL increments and should be estimated and recorded to the nearest 0.1 mL.

**Figure 2.2   Read the bottom of the meniscus. The volume is 23.0 mL.**

## Density

Density is a physical property of a substance and is useful in identifying the substance. **Density** is the ratio of the mass of a substance to the volume occupied by that mass; it is the mass per unit volume and is given by the equations

$$\text{Density} = d = \frac{\text{Mass}}{\text{Volume}} = \frac{m}{V} = \frac{g}{mL} \quad \text{or} \quad \frac{g}{cm^3}$$

In calculating density it is important to make correct use of units and mathematical setups.

**Example Problem:** An object weighs 283.5 g and occupies a volume of 14.6 mL. What is its density?

$$d = \frac{m}{V} = \frac{283.5\,g}{14.6\,mL} = 19.4\,g/mL$$

Note that all the operations involved in the calculation are properly indicated and that all units are shown. If we divide grams by milliliters, we get an answer in grams per milliliter.

The volume of an irregularly shaped object is usually measured by the displacement of a liquid. An object completely submerged in a liquid displaces a volume of the liquid equal to the volume of the object.

Measurement data and calculations must always be accompanied by appropriate units.

## PROCEDURE

**Wear department approved chemical splash goggles and lab coat.**

Record your data on the report form as you complete each measurement, never on a scrap of paper which can be lost or misplaced.

### A.  Temperature

Record all temperatures to the **nearest 0.1°C**.

1. Fill a 250-mL beaker half full of tap water. Place your thermometer in the beaker. Give it at least a minute to reach thermal equilibrium. Keeping the thermometer in the water and holding the tip of the thermometer away from the glass, read and record the temperature.

2. Fill a 150-mL beaker half full of tap water. Set up a ring stand with a small ring and wire gauze at a height so the hottest part of the burner flame will reach the bottom of the beaker. Clamp a large ring to the ring stand so that it is near the middle of the beaker, as shown in Figure 0.3 (page 2), to protect the beaker. Heat the water to boiling. Read and record the temperature of the boiling water, being sure to hold the thermometer away from the bottom of the beaker.

3. Fill a 250-mL beaker one-fourth full of tap water and add a 100-mL beaker of crushed ice. Without stirring, place the thermometer in the beaker, resting it on the bottom. Wait at least 1 minute, then read and record the temperature. Now stir the mixture for about 1 minute. If almost all the ice melts, add more. Read and record the temperature while holding the thermometer off the bottom of the beaker.

### B.  Mass

Record all masses to the nearest ~~0.01g~~ 0.001g.

1. Weigh a 250-mL beaker.

2. Weigh a 125-mL Erlenmeyer flask.

3. Weigh a piece of weighing paper.

4. Add a solid object to the weighing paper from step 3 and record the total mass.

5. Calculate the mass of solid object.

## C. Length

Using a ruler, make the following measurements in both inches and centimeters. Record all lengths to the nearest 0.01cm or 1/32$^{nd}$ of an inch.

1. Measure the length of the line on the right. $\longleftrightarrow$

2. Measure the external height of a 250-mL beaker.

3. Measure the length of a test tube.

## D. Volume

Using the graduated cylinder most appropriate, measure the following volumes to the maximum precision possible. Remember to read the volume at the meniscus.

1. Fill a test tube to the brim with water and measure the volume of the water.

2. Fill a 125-mL Erlenmeyer flask to the brim with water and measure the volume of the water.

3. Measure 5.0 mL of water in a graduated cylinder and pour it into a test tube. With a ruler, measure the height (in cm) and mark the height with a marker.

4. Measure 1.0 mL of water in the graduated cylinder and pour it into a test tube like the one used in the previous step. Again, mark the height with a marker.

In the future, you will often find it convenient to estimate volumes of 1 and 5 mL simply by observing the height of the liquid in the test tube.

## E. Density

Record all volumes to the nearest 0.1 mL and all masses to the nearest 0.01g. Note that you must supply the units for the measurements and calculations in this section.

**1. Density of Water.** Weigh a clean, dry 50-mL graduated cylinder and record its mass. (Graduated cylinders should never be dried over a flame.) Fill the graduated cylinder approximately half-full of water. Record the volume. Reweigh and calculate the density of water.

**2. Density of a Rubber Stopper.** Obtain a rubber stopper. Weigh the dry stopper. Fill a 50-mL graduated cylinder with tap water to approximately half-full. Read and record the exact volume. Carefully place the rubber stopper into the graduated cylinder so that it is fully submerged. Read and record the new volume. Calculate the volume and density of the rubber stopper.

**Return the rubber stopper to your instructor.**

# EXPERIMENT 3

## Density Determination of a Metal

**DISCUSSION**

In this experiment you will collect data for **extensive properties (mass and volume)**, properties that are dependent on the amount of a substance and use them to determine an **intensive property, (density)**, which is independent of the amount of the substance.

Measurements made anywhere always have some amount of uncertainty. The uncertainty is a result of the limitations of the instruments used for data collection and it is always the last digit in a string of numbers. Therefore, measurements in the laboratory must be made with the greatest precision possible.

Precision and accuracy are not the same and they are not interchangeable. Precision is determined by examining several examples of the same measurement and determining the repeatability. The closer these values are to each other the better the precision. Accuracy refers to how close a value is to a true (accepted) value. The closer the experimental value is to the literature (accepted) value, the better the accuracy. It is possible to be very precise and not very accurate. The goal is to have both precision and accuracy.

Chemists often use a device called a pycnometer (Figure 3.1) to determine the density of a substance. We will use a 50-mL Erlenmeyer flask rubber stopper and a short piece of capillary tubing as our pycnometer (Figure 3.2).

In this experiment you will calculate the density of the sample using the equation Density (D) = Mass (M) / Volume (V). You will then use your calculated value of the density to identify the metal from the list given to you in Table 3.2. You will also calculate the percent error using the following equation:

$$\% \text{ error} = \frac{|\text{experimental} - \text{actual}|}{\text{actual value}} \times 100$$

In general, substances to be weighed are not placed directly on a balance pan; the sample is place on weighing paper or in a clean dry beaker. The balance you will be using weighs to the nearest 0.0001g. This balance is so sensitive it will weigh your fingerprints; temperature and air currents will also affect the reading.

You will determine all volumes in this experiment by calculation. By knowing the mass and density of water at a given temperature the volume of water can be calculated, to the nearest 0.0001mL. A direct measurement of all volumes to this number of decimal places is not possible with the equipment you have.

The density of water is given in Table 3.1 on page 24. Notice that the density of water changes as the temperature changes.

**Figure 3.1 Pycnometer.**

**Figure 3.2 Our pycnometer.**

## SAMPLE DATA AND CALCULATIONS:

A student performed the experiment and the following data was collected.

## DATA:

### A. Determination of the volume of a pycnometer

1. Mass of pycnometer       _38.3770_ g

2. Mass of pycnometer + water       _95.3928_ g

3. Temperature of water       _23.0_ °C

4. Density of water       _0.997538_ g/ml (See Table 3.1)

### B. Determination of the density of solid sample

1. Mass of beaker (g)       _52.7597_ g

2. Mass of beaker + sample (g)       _57.6246_ g

3. Mass of pycnometer + water + sample (g)   _99.7628_ g

4. Temperature of water (°C)       _23.0_ °C

5. Density of water (g/ml)       0.997538 g/mL

## CALCULATIONS:

### C. Determination of the volume of a pycnometer

1. Mass of water = (Mass of pycnometer + water) – Mass of pycnometer

   57.0158 g = 95.3928 g – 38.37720 g

2. Volume of water = Mass of water / Density of water

   57.1565 mL = 57.0158 g / 0.997538 g/mL

3. Volume of flask = Volume of water = 57.1565 mL

### D. Determination of the density of solid sample

1. Mass of sample = (Mass of beaker + sample) – Mass of beaker

   4.8649 g = 57.6246 g – 52.7597 g

2. Mass of water = (Mass of pycnometer + water + sample) – Mass of sample – Mass of pycnometer

    56.5209 g = 99.7628 g – 4.8649 g – 38.3770 g

3. Volume of water = Mass of water / Density of water

    56.6604 mL = 56.5209 g / 0.997538 g/mL

4. Volume of sample = Volume of pycnometer – Volume of water

    0.4961 mL = 57.1565 mL – 56.6604 mL

5. Density of sample = Mass of sample / Volume of sample

    9.806g/mL = 4.8649 g / 0.4961 mL

## PROCEDURE

**ALL recorded masses must be determined on the <u>same</u> analytical balance.**

**Record all temperature to the nearest 0.1 °C.**

**Wear department approved chemical splash goggles and lab coat.**

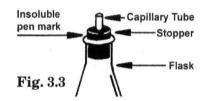

**Fig. 3.3**

### A. Determination of the volume of a pycnometer

1. Carefully insert the stopper in the flask until it fits snugly. Using a water insoluble pen, place a mark all the way around the stopper just on top of the flask (see Figure 3.3 above). This sets the internal volume of the flask. The stopper must be reinserted to this mark every time.

2. Using an analytical balance determine and record the mass of the pycnometer to the nearest 0.0001 g. *0.001g*

3. Fill the flask until it over flows with water. **Carefully remove ALL air bubbles.** You may use a glass stirrer to remove the bubbles. Carefully insert the stopper to the mark made in step A1. The excess water will escape through the hole of the capillary tube. Dry the pycnometer completely. **Make sure that there is no water anywhere on the outside of the pycnometer.**

4. Determine and record the mass of the pycnometer and water on the same balance used in step A2.

5. Remove the stopper, determine and record the temperature of the water to the nearest 0.1°C.

6. Record the density of water at that temperature from Table 3.1.

### B. Determination of the Density of a Solid.

1. Determine and record the mass of a smallest clean dry beaker on the same analytical balance used previously, to the nearest 0.0001 g. *0.001g*

2. Use the electronic balance to add approximately 5 g of the unknown sample to the beaker. Do not record this approximate value. Record the number of the sample on your data sheet.

3. Determine and record the mass of the beaker and sample to the nearest ~~0.0001 g~~ on the same analytical balance you used in step B1.   0.001g

4. Carefully place the entire sample into your pycnometer.

5. Refill the pycnometer with water. **Carefully remove ALL air bubbles.** Carefully insert the stopper to the mark you drew (step A1). The excess water will escape through the hole of the capillary tube. **Completely dry the outside of the pycnometer.**

6. Determine and record the mass of your pycnometer, water and sample to the nearest 0.0001 g.

7. Remove the stopper. Determine and record the temperature of the water to the nearest 0.1°C.

8. Record the density of water at that temperature using Table 3.1.

9. Return the sample to the designated container. This is Run 1.

10. From the same unknown numbered container, weigh approximately 5-g of the dry sample. Repeat B 1 to B 9 for Run 2 and then for Run 3.

**Note:** Do not return the wet samples into the original container.


## TABLE 3.1: Density of water at various temperatures (°C)

To use the table below, run down the left column for whole degrees then move across for tenths of a degree. For example, the density of pure water at 17.7°C = 0.998650 g mL$^{-1}$.

| | 0.0 | 0.1 | 0.2 | 0.3 | 0.4 | 0.5 | 0.6 | 0.7 | 0.8 | 0.9 |
|---|---|---|---|---|---|---|---|---|---|---|
| 15 | 0.999099 | 0.999084 | 0.999069 | 0.999054 | 0.999038 | 0.999023 | 0.999007 | 0.998991 | 0.998975 | 0.998959 |
| 16 | 0.998943 | 0.998926 | 0.998910 | 0.998893 | 0.998877 | 0.998860 | 0.998843 | 0.998826 | 0.998809 | 0.998792 |
| 17 | 0.998774 | 0.998757 | 0.998739 | 0.998722 | 0.998704 | 0.998686 | 0.998668 | 0.998650 | 0.998632 | 0.998613 |
| 18 | 0.998595 | 0.998576 | 0.998558 | 0.998539 | 0.998520 | 0.998501 | 0.998482 | 0.998463 | 0.998444 | 0.998424 |
| 19 | 0.998405 | 0.998385 | 0.998365 | 0.998345 | 0.998325 | 0.998305 | 0.998285 | 0.998265 | 0.998244 | 0.998224 |
| 20 | 0.998203 | 0.998183 | 0.998162 | 0.998141 | 0.998120 | 0.998099 | 0.998078 | 0.998056 | 0.998035 | 0.998013 |
| 21 | 0.997992 | 0.997970 | 0.997948 | 0.997926 | 0.997904 | 0.997882 | 0.997860 | 0.997837 | 0.997815 | 0.997792 |
| 22 | 0.997770 | 0.997747 | 0.997724 | 0.997701 | 0.997678 | 0.997655 | 0.997632 | 0.997608 | 0.997585 | 0.997561 |
| 23 | 0.997538 | 0.997514 | 0.997490 | 0.997466 | 0.997442 | 0.997418 | 0.997394 | 0.997369 | 0.997345 | 0.997320 |
| 24 | 0.997296 | 0.997271 | 0.997246 | 0.997221 | 0.997196 | 0.997171 | 0.997146 | 0.997120 | 0.997095 | 0.997069 |
| 25 | 0.997044 | 0.997018 | 0.996992 | 0.996967 | 0.996941 | 0.996914 | 0.996888 | 0.996862 | 0.996836 | 0.996809 |
| 26 | 0.996783 | 0.996756 | 0.996729 | 0.996703 | 0.996676 | 0.996649 | 0.996621 | 0.996594 | 0.996567 | 0.996540 |
| 27 | 0.996512 | 0.996485 | 0.996457 | 0.996429 | 0.996401 | 0.996373 | 0.996345 | 0.996317 | 0.996289 | 0.996261 |
| 28 | 0.996232 | 0.996204 | 0.996175 | 0.996147 | 0.996118 | 0.996089 | 0.996060 | 0.996031 | 0.996002 | 0.995973 |
| 29 | 0.995944 | 0.995914 | 0.995885 | 0.995855 | 0.995826 | 0.995796 | 0.995766 | 0.995736 | 0.995706 | 0.995676 |
| 30 | 0.995646 | 0.995616 | 0.995586 | 0.995555 | 0.995525 | 0.995494 | 0.995464 | 0.995433 | 0.995402 | 0.995371 |

**Table 3.2: Density and the Specific Heat of Some Metals**

| Metal | Atomic Mass (amu) | Density g/mL | Specific Heat (J/g°C) |
|---|---|---|---|
| Magnesium (Mg) | 24.31 | 1.738 | 1.020 |
| Aluminum (Al) | 26.98 | 2.698 | 0.904 |
| Titanium (Ti) | 47.87 | 4.540 | 0.520 |
| Zinc (Zn) | 65.39 | 7.134 | 0.388 |
| Tin (Sn) | 118.7 | 7.287 | 0.222 |
| Iron (Fe) | 55.84 | 7.874 | 0.449 |
| Nickel (Ni) | 58.69 | 8.912 | 0.445 |
| Copper (Cu) | 63.55 | 8.960 | 0.384 |
| Silver (Ag) | 107.9 | 10.50 | 0.235 |
| Lead (Pb) | 207.2 | 11.34 | 0.127 |
| Palladium (Pd) | 106.4 | 12.02 | 0.240 |
| Gold (Au) | 197.0 | 19.28 | 0.133 |

# EXPERIMENT 4

## Calorimetry and Specific Heat

### MATERIALS

Styrofoam cups, thermometer, graduated cylinder, crucible tongs, large beaker (400 or 600-mL), metal pot

### EQUIPMENT

Hot plate, decigram balance

### CHEMICALS

Metal samples

### SAFETY

Lab coat, chemical splash goggles

*temperature- Average kinetic energy of a substance.*

*Heat - A form of kinetic energy.*

*Specific heat - amount of energy required to raise the temp of 1g of a substance 1°C.*

### DISCUSSION

Calorimetry is the science of measuring a quantity of heat. Heat is a form of energy associated with the motion of atoms or molecules of a substance. Heat (often represented as "$q$") is measured in energy units such as joules or calories. Temperature (often represented as "$T$") is measured in degrees (usually Celsius). The measurement of temperature is already familiar to you. The same temperature is obtained for the water in a lake and for a thermos of water taken from the lake. But the heat content of the whole lake is much more than the heat content in that thermos of water even though both are exactly the same temperature.

Temperature and heat are related to each other by the specific heat (*sp ht*) of a substance, defined as the quantity of heat needed to raise one gram of a substance by one degree Celsius ($J/g°C$). The relationship between quantity of heat ($q$), specific heat (*sp ht*), mass ($m$) and temperature change ($\Delta T$) is mathematically expressed by the equation:

$$q = (m)(sp\,ht)(\Delta T) \quad \text{or} \quad \text{Joules} = (g)\left(\frac{J}{g°C}\right)(°C) = (\cancel{g})\left(\frac{J}{\cancel{g}\cancel{°C}}\right)(\cancel{°C}) = J$$

Since the mass and temperature can be measured by a balance and a thermometer, respectively, $q$ can be calculated if the *sp ht* for a substance is known. Also, *sp ht* can be calculated if the heat content ($q$) of the substance is known. The amount of heat needed to raise the temperature of 1 g of water by 1 degree Celsius is the basis of the calorie. Thus, the specific heat of water is exactly $1.00\,cal/g°C$. The SI unit of energy is the joule and it is related to the calorie by 1 calorie = $4.184$ J. Thus, the specific heat of water is also $4.184\,J/g°C$. The specific heat of a substance relates to its capacity to absorb heat energy. The higher the specific heat of a substance the more energy required to change its temperature.

The specific heat of metals generally varies with their atomic masses. You will see this relationship later when the data, from Table 3.2, is graphed. For this data, atomic mass is the independent variable and specific heat is the dependent variable because we are examining how specific heat changes as a function of atomic mass. **For a review of variables and graphing techniques, see Study Aid 2.**

In this experiment, we will use calorimetry to determine the specific heat of a metal. Heat energy is transferred from a hot metal to water until the metal and the water have reached the same temperature. This transfer is done in an insulated container to minimize heat losses to the surroundings. We then make the assumption that all the heat lost by the metal ($q_x$) was absorbed by the water and is equal to the heat gained by the water, ($q_w$). Since we know the specific heat of water, we have all the variables needed to calculate $q_w$ using the equation:

$$q_w = (m_w)(sp\ ht_w)(\Delta T_w)$$

Since Heat Gained by Water is equal to Heat Lost by Metal ($q_w = -q_x$) and $q_x = (m_x)(sp\ ht_x)(\Delta Tx)$, we can calculate the specific heat capacity ($sp\ ht_x$) of a metal.

## Sample Calculation:

A metal sample weighing 68.3820 g was heated to 99.0°C, then quickly transferred into a styrofoam calorimeter containing 62.5515 g of distilled water at a temperature of 18.0°C. The temperature of the water in the styrofoam cup increased and stabilized at 20.6°C. Calculate the $sp\ ht_x$ and identify the metal using 4.184 J/g°C for the $sp\ ht_w$.

$\Delta T_w = 20.6°C - 18.0°C = 2.6°C$

$q_w = (m_w)(sp\ ht_w)(\Delta T_w)$

$\quad = (62.5515g)(4.184J/g°C)(2.6°C)$

$\quad = 680\ J \quad$ (heat absorbed by the water)

Let $x$ be the metal. Then, since all of the heat absorbed by the water came from the hot metal, we can say that

$q_w = -q_x = (m_x)(sp\ ht_x)\Delta T_x$

$\Delta T_x = 20.6°C - 99.0°C = -78.4°C$

$680\ J = -(68.3820g)(sp\ ht_x)(-78.4°C)$

$sp\ ht_x = 0.13J/g°C$

Refer to Table 3.2 and determine that the unknown metal is lead or gold.

**PROCEDURE**

**Wear department approved chemical splash goggles and lab coat.**

Record all the temperatures to the **nearest 0.1 ˚C**.

Record all the masses to the **nearest 0.01 g**.

1. Stack two dry Styrofoam cups together, weigh them and record their mass on the data sheet.

2. Using your graduated cylinder add about ~~100~~ 75 ml of water to the inner Styrofoam cup. Weigh and record the mass of the Styrofoam cups and water.

3. Place the nested cups in a large beaker. The beaker is used to keep the nested cups, water and thermometer from falling over.

4. Measure and record the initial temperature of the water, $T_w$, in the Styrofoam cup.

5. Take the entire setup (beaker, Styrofoam cups and water) to the fume hood. Record the number of an unknown metal sample. Record the temperature of this sample (record the temperature of water in which your sample is being heated, this is $T_m$). Using crucible tongs, quickly and carefully transfer ~~two to three~~ one pieces of the heated metals to your cups. Try to avoid any splashing.

6. Return to your bench. Stir the water gently and constantly. Check the temperature every 10 to 15 seconds. Record the highest temperature. (This is the final temperature for both the metal and water, $T_f$.)

7. Measure and record the mass of the cups, water and sample.

8. Dispose water into the sink and return the metal to the designated place. ,beaker on the right **DO NOT** return the sample into the hot water bath.

9. Use the same Styrofoam cups and repeat steps 2 to 8 for Trial 2 ~~and again for Trial 3~~. For each trial, make sure you pick ~~two to three~~ one pieces of the heated metals from the same unknown-number container.

## REPORT FOR EXPERIMENT 4

# Calorimetry and Specific Heat

*Show all calculations. Answer with proper number of significant figures and units. Answer all the questions in completed sentences.*

**Data:**

**UNKNOWN SAMPLE Number:** _____
(same as Experiment 3, density determination of a metal)

|  | TRIAL 1 | TRIAL 2 | TRIAL 3 |
|---|---|---|---|
| 1) Mass of Styrofoam Cups (nearest 0.01 g) | 4.52 g | 4.52 g | _____ |
| 2) Mass of Styrofoam Cups + Water (100 mL) (nearest 0.01 g) | 74.60 g | 76.09 g | _____ |
| 3) Initial Water Temperature, $T_w$ (nearest 0.1°C) | 21.5°C | 21.3°C | _____ |
| 4) Initial Temperature of the heated metal, $T_m$ (nearest 0.1°C) | 99.5°C | 99.0°C | _____ |
| 5) Highest Temperature reached by metal + Water ($T_f$), (nearest 0.1°C) | 25.3°C | 25.4°C | _____ |
| 6) Mass of Styrofoam Cups + Water + Metal (nearest 0.01 g) | 97.86 g | 97.94 g | _____ |

**DO NOT FORGET TO WRITE DOWN ALL THE PROPER UNITS AND SIGNIFICANT FIGURES FOR YOUR MEASUREMENTS**

## Calculations:  Show all calculations

|  | TRIAL 1 | TRIAL 2 | TRIAL 3 |
|---|---|---|---|

1) Mass of Water ($m_w$)             70.08g    71.57g    _____

Trial 1                    Trial 2

74.60                      76.09
- 4.52                    - 4.52
70.08 g                    71.57g

2) Change in temperature of Water ($\Delta T_w$)      3.8°C     4.1°C     _____
   $\Delta T_w = T_f - T_w$

Trial 1                    Trial 2

25.3                       25.4
-21.5                     -21.3
3.8°C                      4.1°C

3) Heat Gained by water ($q_w$):             1,114 J    1,227 J    _____

(Given: Specific Heat of Water  = $sp\ ht_w$ = 4.184 J/g°C)

$q_w = (m_w)(sp\ ht_w)(\Delta T_w)$

Trial 1

$q_w = (70.08g)(4.184\ J/g°C)(3.8°C) = 1,114\ J$

Trial 2

$q_w = (71.57g)(4.184\ J/g°C)(4.1°C) = 1,227\ J$

4) Mass of Metal Sample ($m_x$)             23.26g    21.85g    _____

Trial 1                    Trial 2

97.86                      97.94
-74.60                    - 76.09
23.26g                     21.85g

|  | TRIAL 1 | TRIAL 2 | TRIAL 3 |
|---|---|---|---|
| 5) Change in temperature of Metal ($\Delta T_x$) $\Delta T_x = T_f - T_m$ | -74.2°C | -73.6°C | |

Trial 1          Trial 2

          25.4

25.3          -99.0

-99.5          ‾‾‾‾‾

‾‾‾‾‾          -73.6

-74.2

6) Specific heat of the unknown metal sample ($sp\ ht_x$)    655.3 J/g°C    766.9 J/g°C    _____

Hint:    $q_w = -q_x$ = Heat Gained by Water = Heat Lost by Metal

$q_x = (m_x)(sp\ ht_x)(\Delta T_x)$

Trial 1

$\dfrac{1.114 J}{1.7} = \dfrac{-(23.26 g)(sp\ ht_x)(-74.2c)}{1.7} = \dfrac{(1.7)(sp\ ht_x)}{1.7}$

$sp\ ht_x = 655.3\ J/g°C$

Trial 2

$\dfrac{1.227 J}{1.6} = \dfrac{-(21.85 g)(sp\ ht_x)(-73.6°C)}{1.6} = \dfrac{(1.6)(sp\ ht_x)}{1.6}$

$sp\ ht_x = 766.9\ J/g°C$

    655.3
  +766.9
  ‾‾‾‾‾‾
  1.4 J/g°C

Average $sp\ ht_x$: ___1.4 J/g°C___

Average density (from Experiment 3): ___1.738 g/mL___

$$\% \ error = \frac{|theory - Expected|}{theory} \times 100$$

7) Calculate the percent error of your measured specific heat of the metal sample.

$$\% \ error = \frac{|1.4 - 1.020|}{1.4} \times 100$$

$$\boxed{38\%}$$

8) Identify the metal and state your reason, in full sentences.

The metal is magnesium because it had the closest specific heat to my results.

**REPORT FOR EXPERIMENT 4 (continued)**     **NAME** _____

## QUESTIONS AND PROBLEMS

1. The water in the calorimeter gets its heat energy from the ___*from the metal* ~~calorimeter~~ sample___.

2. Why is it important for there to be enough water in the calorimeter to completely cover the metal sample?

   *So no air is absorbed. if there is air exposed to the metal, it'll change the results.*

3. What is the specific heat in J/g°C for a metal sample with a mass of 95.6 g which absorbs 841 J of energy when its temperature increases from 30.0°C to 98.0°C?

   $841 J = (95.6 g)(sp ht)(68°C)$

   $841 J = (95.6 g)(sp ht)(68°C)$

   $\dfrac{841}{(68)(95.6)} = \boxed{0.13 J/g°C}$

4. Results of scientific experiments must be reproducible when repeated or they do not mean anything. When results are repeated, the experiment is said to have good **precision**. When the results agree with a theoretical value they are described as **accurate**. Which is better, the precision or the accuracy of the experimental specific heats determined for your metal sample? Support your answer with your data.

   *The precision is more important because we did multiple trials for the experiment. even tho everything was the same in both trials, we still got different results for each.*

Analysis of the relationship between the atomic mass and the specific heat of some metals via graphing:

Use the data presented in Table 3.2 to answer questions a–d and then complete the graph (question e). Construct the graph following the guidelines provided in Study Aid 2.

    a.  What is the independent variable? <u>Atomic Mass</u>

    b.  What is the dependent variable? <u>Specific Heat</u>

    c.  In Table 3.2, what is the range of values for atomic mass?

           <u>182.89 amu</u>         207.2 − 24.31

    d.  In Table 3.2, what is the range of values for specific heat?

           <u>.893 J/g°C</u>        1.020 −0.127

    e.  Use the graphing paper located at the end of the lab manual plot the data in Table 3.2. Be sure to include the following:

        i.     A title

        ii.    Placement of the independent and dependent variables on the appropriate axes

        iii.   Increments for each axis

        iv.   Labels (including the units) for each axis

        v.    All the data points

    f.  Use your graph to summarize the relationship between the atomic mass of metal atoms and the specific heat of a metal.

           As the atomic mass increases, the specific heat decreases.

    g.  The specific heat was measured for two unknown metal samples. The first sample tested had a specific heat of 0.68 J/g°C. The second metal had a specific heat of 0.35 J/g°C. Use your graph to estimate the atomic masses of these two metals.

           first metal- atomic mass    Specific heat

                   <u>3⊘ |35 amu|</u>      <u>0.68 J/g°C</u>

           Second metal- atomic mass    Specific heat

                    <u>|68 amu|</u>      <u>0.35 J/g°C</u>

# EXPERIMENT 5

## Freezing Points

**MATERIALS**

Crushed ice, thermometer, watch or clock with second hand, slotted stoppers, large test tube, beaker (250 or 400-mL), large ring clamp labeled spatula

**EQUIPMENT**

Balance (0.01g)

**CHEMICALS**

Glacial acetic acid ($HC_2H_3O_2$), Benzoic acid ($C_6H_5COOH$)

**SAFETY**

Chemical splash goggles and lab coat

**DISCUSSION**

All pure substances, elements and compounds, possess unique physical and chemical properties. Just as one human being can be distinguished from all others by certain characteristics—fingerprints or DNA, for example—it is also possible, through knowledge of its properties, to distinguish any given compound from among the many millions that are known.

### A.  Melting and Freezing Points of Pure Substances.

The melting point and the boiling point are easily determined physical properties that are very useful in identifying a substance. Consequently, these properties are almost always recorded when a compound is described in the chemical literature (textbooks, handbooks, journal articles, etc.). The freezing and melting of a pure substance occurs at the same temperature, measured when the liquid and solid phases of the substance are in equilibrium. When energy is being removed from a liquid in equilibrium with its solid, the process is called freezing; when energy is being added to a solid in equilibrium with its liquid, the process is called melting.

$$\text{liquid} \quad \underset{\underset{\text{melting}}{\xrightarrow{\hspace{2cm} + \text{ energy}}}}{\overset{\overset{\text{freezing}}{\underset{- \text{ energy}}{\xrightarrow{\hspace{2cm}}}}}{\rightleftharpoons}} \quad \text{solid}$$

In this experiment, we will determine the freezing point of a pure organic compound, glacial acetic acid ($HC_2H_3O_2$). When the experimental freezing point has been determined, it will be compared with the melting point temperature listed in the *Handbook of Chemistry and Physics*.

When heat is removed from a liquid, the liquid particles lose kinetic energy and move more slowly causing the temperature of the liquid to decrease. Finally enough heat is removed and the particles move so slowly that the liquid becomes a solid, often a crystalline solid. The temperature when this happens (the freezing point) is different for different substances.

The amount of energy removed from a quantity of liquid to freeze it, is equal to the amount of energy added to the same quantity of its solid to melt it. Thus, depending on the direction of energy flow, this equilibrium temperature is called the melting point or the freezing point.

## B.    Freezing Point of Impure Substances

When a substance (solvent) is uniformly mixed with a small amount of another substance (solute), the freezing point of the resulting solution (an "impure substance") will be lower than that of the pure solvent. This particular property of a solution is called freezing point depression. For example, the accepted freezing point for pure water is 0.0°C. Solutions of salt in water may freeze at temperatures as low as –21°C depending on the amount of salt added to the water. Antifreeze is added to the water in a car radiator to lower the freezing point of the water.

Melting point/freezing point data are of great value in determining the identity and/or purity of substances, especially in the field of organic chemistry. If a sample of a compound melts or freezes appreciably below the known melting point of the pure substance, we know that the sample contains impurities which have lowered the melting point. If the melting point of an unknown compound agrees with that of a known compound, the identity can often be confirmed by mixing the unknown compound with the known and determining the melting point of the mixture. If the melting point of the mixture is the same as that of the known compound, the compounds are identical. On the other hand, a lower melting point for the mixture indicates that the two compounds are not identical.

## C.    Supercooling During Freezing

Frequently when a substance is being cooled, the temperature will fall below the true freezing point before crystals begin to form. This phenomenon is known as supercooling because the substance is cooled below its freezing point without forming a solid. Supercooling is more likely to occur if the liquid remains very still and undisturbed as its temperature is lowered. When the system is disturbed in any way, for example, by stirring or jarring, crystallization occurs rapidly throughout the system. As the crystals form, heat is released (called the heat of crystallization) and the temperature rises quickly to the freezing point of the substance. Thus, supercooling does not change the freezing point of the substance.

## D.    Freezing Point Determinations

You will do three freezing point determinations during this experiment using the setup in Figure 5.1.

**Trial 1.**    Freezing point determination of pure glacial acetic acid WITH STIRRING. This will usually eliminate supercooling.

**Trial 2.**    Freezing point determination of pure glacial acetic acid WITHOUT STIRRING. This should enhance the possibility of supercooling but does not guarantee it.

**Trial 3.**  Freezing point determination of acetic acid (the solvent) after benzoic acid (a solute) has been dissolved in it. This will be done WITHOUT STIRRING to enhance super-cooling again.

The time/temperature data will be graphed and the freezing point for each trial read from the graph.


## PROCEDURE

**Wear department approved chemical splash goggles and lab coat.**

---

Notes:   Since water and other contaminants will influence the freezing points in this experiment, use only clean, dry equipment.

 Glacial acetic acid is concentrated acid with irritating vapor. Avoid skin contact with your skin.

Read and record all temperatures to the nearest 0.1°C.

---

### A.   Freezing Point Determination of Pure Glacial Acetic Acid

**(Note: the freezing point of glacial acetic acid is 16.5°C.)**

**Trial 1:** With stirring

1. Fasten a utility clamp to the top of a clean, dry test tube. Position this clamp-tube assembly on a ring stand so that the bottom of the tube is about 20 cm above the ring stand base.

2. Obtain a split one–hole stopper and copper stirring rod.  The stopper is used to suspend the thermometer and contain the vapors.  It IS NOT inserted into the test tube at ANY TIME. Insert a thermometer in the stopper and position it in the test tube so that the end of the bulb is about 1.5 cm from the bottom of the test tube. Turn the thermometer so that the tempera-ture scale can be read in the slot.

3. Take only your test tube to the fume hood.  Measure out about 10 mL of glacial acetic acid using the graduated cylinder provided (DO NOT remove the graduated cylinder form the hood.) Pour the acid into your test tube. **Glacial acetic acid is irritating and harmful if inhaled so keep the stopper/thermometer assembly in place while working at your bench.**

4. Reclamp the test tube to your ring stand to minimize the risk of spilling. Make sure the thermometer bulb is covered by the acid and adjust the temperature of the acetic acid to approx-imately 25°C (between 23°C and 27°C) by warming or cooling the tube in a beaker of water.

5. Fill a 400 mL beaker about three-quarters full of crushed ice; add cold water until the ice is almost covered. Position the beaker of ice and water on the ring stand base under the clamped tube-thermometer assembly. The ice bath can be reused through out the entire exper-iment.  Add more ice if it is needed. Don't forget to place a safety ring around the beaker.

6. Read the temperature of the acetic acid and record as the 0.0 minute time reading in the Data Table. Record 5 temperature values, at 30 second intervals, with the acetic acid above the ice–H$_2$O mixture. As soon as you record the 5th temperature reading, loosen the clamp on the

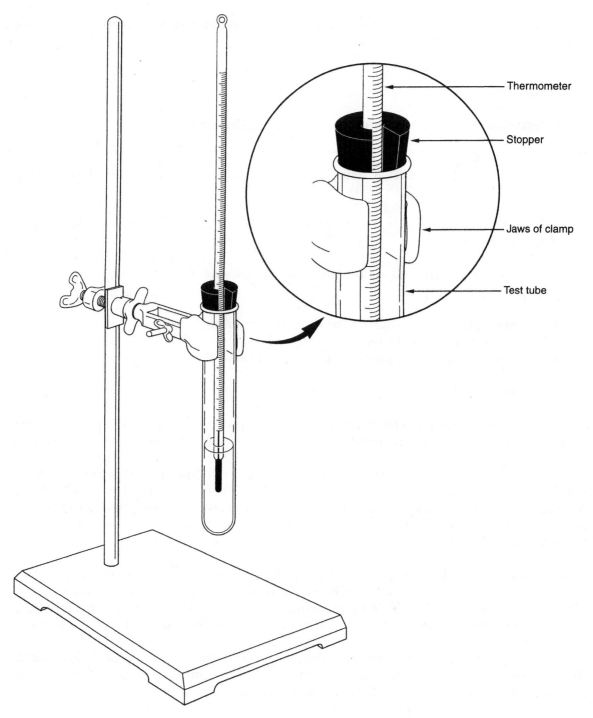

**Figure 5.1   Setup for freezing-point determination**

ring stand and lower the clamped tube-thermometer assembly so that all of the acetic acid in the tube is below the surface of the ice water. Fasten the clamp to hold the tube in this position.

7. Stir the acetic acid with the copper stirrer (during trial 1 only), keeping the bulb of the thermometer completely immersed in the acid. Continue the temperature readings at 30-second intervals as the acid cools. Circle the temperature reading when the crystals were first observed.

8. Continue to take temperature readings at 30-second intervals (with constant stirring for trial #1) until a total time of 12 minutes has elapsed or until the entire volume of liquid becomes solidified. After that occurs, read the temperature for an additional 2 minutes (4 time intervals) and continue with the next step.

9. After completing the temperature readings, remove the test tube-thermometer assembly from the ice bath, keeping the thermometer and the copper stirrer in place. Immerse the lower portion of the test tube in a beaker of warm water to melt the frozen acetic acid. **Do not discard this acid**; it will be used in Trials 2 and 3.

**Trial 2:** Without stirring

10. Repeat steps 4–9 with the following changes:

    a. Add more ice to the ice bath if needed as in step 5.

    b. After submerging the tube in the ice bath, do NOT stir. Do NOT touch or move the apparatus in any way.

    c. If the temperature goes down to about 4°C or lower without the formation of acetic acid crystals and remains there, scratch the inside wall of the test tube with the copper stirrer. When you do this be very observant of the temperature changes. Continue to record temperature readings for the full 12 minutes or until the temperature stabilizes and the liquid is completely solidified.

## B. Freezing Point Determination of An Acetic Acid/Benzoic Acid Solution

 **Trial 3:** Without stirring

11. Weigh approximately 0.50 g (between 0.48 and 0.52 g) of benzoic acid crystals. Now remove the thermometer and the copper stirrer from the test tube of acetic acid and lay them on a piece of clean and dry paper towel on the table. Make sure that the table is clean and dry so that you do not contaminate the thermometer and the copper stirrer or lose any acid. Carefully add all of the benzoic acid to the acetic acid. Stir gently with the thermometer until all of the crystals have dissolved. Stir for an additional minute or two to ensure a uniform solution.

12. Repeat step 10.

13. Warm the test tube to change the solid to a liquid and dispose of the acetic   acid/benzoic acid solution in the waste container provided. Rinse the test tube, thermometer, and copper stirrer with water.

## C. Graphing Temperature Data

Graph the three sets of data using the graph paper or prepare a computer graph. If necessary, review the instructions for preparing a graph in Study Aid 2.

# EXPERIMENT 6

## Water in Hydrates

### MATERIALS

Clay triangle, crucible, cover, ring stand, small ring clamp, Bunsen burner, crucible tongs, balance brush

### EQUIPMENT

Balance (0.01 and 0.0001 g)

### SAFETY

Chemical splash goggles, lab coat

### DISCUSSION

Many salts form compounds in which a definite number of moles of water are combined with each mole of the anhydrous salt. Such compounds are called **hydrates**. The water which is chemically combined in a hydrate is referred to as **water of crystallization** or **water of hydration**. The following are representative examples:

$$CaSO_4 \cdot 2H_2O, \quad CoCl_2 \cdot 6H_2O, \quad MgSO_4 \cdot 7H_2O, \quad Na_2CO_3 \cdot 10H_2O$$

In a hydrate the water molecules are distinct parts of the compound but are joined to it by bonds that are weaker than either those forming the anhydrous salt or those forming the water molecules. In the formula of a hydrate a dot is commonly used to separate the formula of the anhydrous salt from the number of molecules of water of crystallization. For example, the formula of calcium sulfate dihydrate is written $CaSO_4 \cdot 2H_2O$ rather than $CaSO_6H_4$.

Hydrated salts can usually be converted to the anhydrous form by careful heating:

$$\text{Hydrated salt} \xrightarrow{\Delta} \text{Anhydrous salt} + \text{water}$$

Hydrated salts can be studied qualitatively and quantitatively. In the **qualitative** part of this experiment we will observe some of properties of the liquid (water) driven off by heating the sample. In the **quantitative** part of the experiment we will determine **how much** water was in the hydrate by measuring the amount of water driven off by heating.

To insure that all of the water in the original sample has been driven off, chemists use a technique known as **heating to constant weight**. Since time expended for this is limited, constant weight is essentially achieved when the sample is heated and weighed in successive heatings until the weight differs by no more than .005 g. Thus, if the second weighing is no more than .005 g less than the first heating, a third heating is not necessary because the sample has been heated to constant weight (almost). This is a very good reason to follow directions meticulously when heating. If the sample is not heated long enough or at the correct temperature, all of the water may not be driven off completely in the first heating.

Hence it is possible to determine the percentage of water in a hydrated salt by determining the amount of mass lost (water driven off) when a known mass of the hydrate is heated to constant weight.

$$\text{Percentage water} = \left( \frac{\text{Mass lost}}{\text{Mass of sample}} \right)(100)$$

## PROCEDURE

**Wear department approved chemical splash goggles and lab coat.**

> **Note:** At excessively high temperatures anhydrous salt decomposes.

**Quantitative Determination of Water in a Hydrate**

> NOTES:
>
> 1. **Weigh crucible and contents to the nearest 0.0001 g.**
>
> 2. Since there is some inaccuracy in any balance, use the same balance for successive weighings of the same sample. When subtractions are made to give mass of sample and mass lost, the inaccuracy due to the balance should cancel out.
>
> 3. Handle crucibles and covers with tongs only, after initial heating.
>
> 4. Be sure crucibles are at or near room temperature when weighed.
>
> 5. **Record all data directly on the report form as soon as you obtain them.**

1. Place a crucible with cover on a clay triangle; adjust the cover so that is slightly ajar. Heat the empty crucible and cover for 5 minutes. Let it cool down to room temperature.

2. Obtain a sample of an unknown hydrate, as directed by your instructor. Be sure to record the identifying number.

3. Separately weigh and record the mass of the crucible and cover (from step 1) to the nearest 0.0001g.

4. Place between 2 and 3 g of the unknown into the weighed crucible. Cover and weigh the crucible and contents. Record the mass to the nearest 0.0001 g.

5. Place the covered crucible on a clay triangle; adjust the cover so that is slightly ajar, to allow the water vapor to escape (see Figure 6.1); and very gently heat the crucible for 5 minutes.

6. Readjust the flame so that a sharp, inner-blue cone is formed. Heat the crucible for 12 minutes with the tip of the inner-blue cone just touching the bottom of the crucible. The crucible bottom should become dull red during this period.

7. After this first heating is completed, close the cover, cool to room temperature (about 10 minutes), and weigh. Record the mass to the nearest 0.0001 g.

8. To determine if all the water in the sample was removed during the initial heating, reheat the covered crucible and contents for an additional 6 minutes at maximum temperature; cool and reweigh. Record the mass to the nearest 0.0001 g.

9. Compare the mass recorded from steps 7 and 8. If the sample were heated to constant weight, the results of these two weighings should agree within 0.005 g. If the decrease in mass between these two weighings is greater than 0.005 g, repeat the heating and weighing until the results of two successive weighings agree to within 0.005 g.

10. Calculate the percentage of water in your sample on the basis of the final weighing.

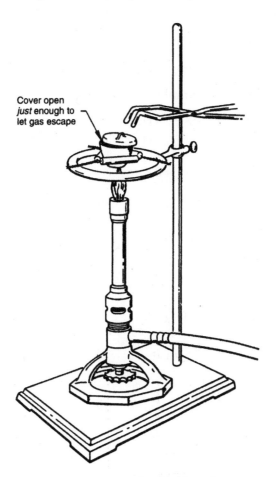

Cover open *just* enough to let gas escape

**Figure 6.1 Method of heating
a crucible**

NAME _____

LAB PARTNER(S) _____

DATE _____

# REPORT FOR EXPERIMENT 6

## Water in Hydrates

**Quantitative Determination of Water in a Hydrate**

Record all masses to the nearest 0.0001 g          **Sample No.** _____

1. Mass of crucible                                                                    _____

2. Mass of cover                                                                       _____

3. Mass of crucible, cover, and sample                                 _____

4. Mass of crucible and cover and sample after 1$^{st}$ heating      _____

5. Mass of crucible and cover and sample after 2$^{nd}$ heating      _____

6. Mass of crucible and cover and sample after 3$^{rd}$ heating
   (if needed)                                                                          _____

7. Mass of original sample
   Show calculation setup:                                                    _____

8. Total mass lost by sample during heating                        _____
   Show calculation setup:

9. Percentage water in the sample          **Sample No.** _____
   Show calculation setup:

                                                                                          _____

## QUESTIONS AND PROBLEMS

*Show all calculations. Answer with proper number of significant figures and units. Answer all the questions in completed sentences.*

**Quantitative Determination of Water in a Hydrate**

1. When the unknown was heated, could the decrease in mass have been partly due to the loss of some substance other than water? Explain.

2. A student heated a hydrated salt sample with an initial mass of 4.8702 g, After the first heating, the mass had decreased to 2.5801 g.
   (a) If the sample was heated to constant weight after the second heating, what is the minimum mass that the sample can have after the second weighing? Show how you determined your answer.

   _____

   (b) The student determined that the mass lost by the sample was 2.2895. What was the percent water in the original hydrated sample? Show all calculations.

   _____

# EXPERIMENT 7

## Lewis Structures and Molecular Models

### MATERIALS AND EQUIPMENT

**Special equipment:** Ball-and-stick molecular model sets

### DISCUSSION

Molecules are stable groups of covalently bonded atoms, usually nonmetallic atoms. Chemists study models of molecules to learn more about their bonds, the spatial relationships between atoms and the shapes of molecules. Using models helps us to predict molecular structure.

### A.  Valence Electrons

Every atom has a nucleus surrounded by electrons which are held within a region of space by the attractive force of the positive protons in the nucleus. The electrons in the outermost energy level of an atom are called valence electrons. The **valence electrons** are involved in bonding atoms together to form compounds. For the representative elements, the number of valence electrons in the outermost energy level is the same as their group number in the periodic table (Groups 1A–7A). For example, sulfur in Group 6A has six valence electrons and potassium in Group 1A has one valence electron.

### B.  Lewis Structures

Lewis electron dot structures are a useful device for keeping track of valence electrons for the representative elements. In this notation, the nucleus and core electrons are represented by the atomic symbol and the valence electrons are represented by dots around the symbol. Although there are exceptions, Lewis structures emphasize an octet of electrons arranged in the noble gas configuration, $ns^2np^6$. Lewis structures can be drawn for individual atoms, monatomic ions, molecules, and polyatomic ions.

1. **Atoms and Monatomic Ions:**  A Lewis structure for an atom shows its symbol surrounded by dots to represent its valence electrons. Monatomic ions form when an atom loses or gains electrons to achieve a noble gas electron configuration. The Lewis structure for a monatomic ion is enclosed by brackets with the charge of the ion shown. The symbol is surrounded by the valence electrons with the number adjusted for the electrons lost or gained when the ion is formed. This is the basis of ionic bond formation which is not included in this experiment.

|  | sulfur atom | sulfide ion | potassium atom | potassium ion |
|---|---|---|---|---|
| Examples: | $:\overset{\cdot\cdot}{\underset{\cdot\cdot}{S}}\cdot$ | $[:\overset{\cdot\cdot}{\underset{\cdot\cdot}{S}}:]^{2-}$ | K· | $[K]^+$ |

2. **Molecules and Polyatomic Ions:**  Lewis structures for molecules and polyatomic ions emphasize the principle that atoms in covalently bonded groups achieve the noble gas configuration, $ns^2np^6$. Since all noble gases except helium have eight valence electrons, this is often

called the octet rule. Although many molecules and ions have structures which support the octet rule, it is only a guideline. There are many exceptions. One major exception is the hydrogen atom which can covalently bond with only one atom and share a total of two electrons to form a noble gas configuration like helium. All of the examples in this experiment follow the octet rule except hydrogen.

A Lewis structure for covalently bonded atoms is a two-dimensional model in which one pair of shared electrons between two atoms is a single covalent bond represented by a short line; unshared or lone pairs of electrons are shown as dots. Sometimes two pairs of electrons are shared between two atoms forming a double bond and are represented by two short lines. It is even possible for two atoms to share three pairs of electrons forming a triple bond, represented by three short lines. For a polyatomic ion, the rules are the same except that the group of atoms is enclosed in brackets and the overall charge of the ion is shown. For example:

The rules for writing Lewis structures for molecules and polyatomic ions will be provided in the procedure section so you can use your Lewis structures to build three-dimensional models.

## C.  Molecular Model Building

The three-dimensional structure of a molecule is difficult to visualize from a two-dimensional Lewis structure. Therefore, in this experiment, a ball-and-stick model kit (molecular "tinker toys") is used to build models so the common geometric patterns into which atoms are arranged can be seen. Each model that is constructed must be checked by the instructor and described by its geometry and its bond angles on the report form.

## D.  Molecular Geometry

Atoms in a molecule or polyatomic ion are arranged into geometric patterns that allow their electron pairs to get as far away from each other as possible (which minimizes the repulsive forces between them). The theory underlying this molecular model is known as the **Valence Shell Electron Pair Repulsion (VSEPR) theory**. All of the geometric structures in this experiment fall into the following patterns:

1. **Tetrahedral:** four pairs of shared electrons (no pairs of lone (unshared) electrons) around a central atom.

2. **Trigonal pyramidal:**  three pairs of shared electrons and one pair of unshared electrons around a central atom.

3. **Trigonal planar:**  three groups of shared electrons around a central atom. Two of these groups are single bonds and one group is a double bond made up of two pairs of shared electrons. There are no unshared electrons around the central atom.

4. **Bent:** two groups of shared electrons (in single or double bonds) and one or two pairs of unshared electrons around a central atom.

5. **Linear:** two groups of shared electrons, usually double bonds with two shared electron pairs between two atoms, and no unshared electrons around a central atom. When there are only two atoms in a molecule or ion, and there is no central atom (HBr, for example), the geometry is also linear. These patterns are described more extensively in Section E, which follows.

---

**Note:** There are other electron arrangements and molecular geometries. Since they do not follow the octet rule, they are not included in this experiment.

---

## E. Bond Angles

Bond angles always refer to the angle formed between two end atoms with respect to the **CENTRAL ATOM**. If there is **no central atom**, there is **no bond angle**.

The size of the angle depends mainly on the repulsive forces of the electrons around the central atom. The molecular model kits are designed so that these angles can be determined when sticks representing electron pairs are inserted into pre-drilled holes.

1. Bond angles for atoms bonded to a central atom without unshared electrons on the central atom.

    a. For four pairs of shared electrons around a central atom (tetrahedral geometry) the angle between the bonds is approximately **109.5°**.

    b. For three atoms bonded to a central atom, (trigonal planar) the angle is **120°**. The shared electron pairs can be arranged in single or double bonds.

    c. For two atoms bonded to a central atom (linear) the angle is **180°**. The shared electrons are usually arranged in double bonds.

    d. Linear diatomic molecules or ions do not have a central atom. Therefore, they do not have a bond angle.

2. Bond angles for atoms bonded to a central atom **with** unshared electrons on the central atom.

When some of the valence electrons around a central atom are unshared, the VSEPR theory can be used to predict changes in spatial arrangements. An unshared pair of electrons on the central atom has a strong influence on the shape of the molecule. It reduces the angle of bonding pairs by squeezing them toward each other.

Note: The unshared pairs reduce the bond angle between the bonded atoms. For example:

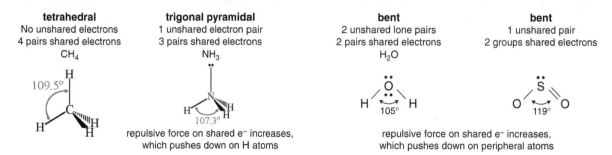

| tetrahedral | trigonal pyramidal | bent | bent |
|---|---|---|---|
| No unshared electrons | 1 unshared electron pair | 2 unshared lone pairs | 1 unshared pair |
| 4 pairs shared electrons | 3 pairs shared electrons | 2 pairs shared electrons | 2 groups shared electrons |
| $CH_4$ | $NH_3$ | $H_2O$ | |

repulsive force on shared e⁻ increases, which pushes down on H atoms

repulsive force on shared e⁻ increases, which pushes down on peripheral atoms

## F.  Bond Polarity

Electrons shared by two atoms are influenced by the positive attractive forces of both atomic nuclei. For like atoms, these forces are equal. For example, in diatomic molecules such as $H_2$ or $Cl_2$ the bonded atoms have exactly the same electronegativity (affinity for the bonding electrons). Electronegativity values for most of the elements have been assigned.

H—H

:C̈l—C̈l:

### Electronegativity Table

| Atomic number | 9 |
|---|---|
| Symbol | F |
| Electronegativity | 4.0 |

| 1 H 2.1 | | | | | | | | | | | | | | | | | 2 He |
|---|---|---|---|---|---|---|---|---|---|---|---|---|---|---|---|---|---|
| 3 Li 1.0 | 4 Be 1.5 | | | | | | | | | | | 5 B 2.0 | 6 C 2.5 | 7 N 3.0 | 8 O 3.5 | 9 F 4.0 | 10 Ne |
| 11 Na 0.9 | 12 Mg 1.2 | | | | | | | | | | | 13 Al 1.5 | 14 Si 1.8 | 15 P 2.1 | 16 S 2.5 | 17 Cl 3.0 | 18 Ar |
| 19 K 0.8 | 20 Ca 1.0 | 21 Sc 1.3 | 22 Ti 1.4 | 23 V 1.6 | 24 Cr 1.6 | 25 Mn 1.5 | 26 Fe 1.8 | 27 Co 1.8 | 28 Ni 1.8 | 29 Cu 1.9 | 30 Zn 1.6 | 31 Ga 1.6 | 32 Ge 1.8 | 33 As 2.0 | 34 Se 2.4 | 35 Br 2.8 | 36 Kr |
| 37 Rb 0.8 | 38 Sr 1.0 | 39 Y 1.2 | 40 Zr 1.4 | 41 Nb 1.6 | 42 Mo 1.8 | 43 Tc 1.9 | 44 Ru 2.2 | 45 Rh 2.2 | 46 Pd 2.2 | 47 Ag 1.9 | 48 Cd 1.7 | 49 In 1.7 | 50 Sn 1.8 | 51 Sb 1.9 | 52 Te 2.1 | 53 I 2.5 | 54 Xe |
| 55 Cs 0.7 | 56 Ba 0.9 | 57–71 La–Lu 1.1–1.2 | 72 Hf 1.3 | 73 Ta 1.5 | 74 W 1.7 | 75 Re 1.9 | 76 Os 2.2 | 77 Ir 2.2 | 78 Pt 2.2 | 79 Au 2.4 | 80 Hg 1.9 | 81 Tl 1.8 | 82 Pb 1.8 | 83 Bi 1.9 | 84 Po 2.0 | 85 At 2.2 | 86 Rn |
| 87 Fr 0.7 | 88 Ra 0.9 | 89–103 Ac–Lr 1.1–1.7 | 104 Rf — | 105 Db — | 106 Sg — | 107 Bh — | 108 Hs — | 109 Mt — | 110 Ds — | 111 Rg — | | | | | | | |

\* The electronegativity value is given below the symbol of each element.

In general, electronegativity increases as we move across a period and up a group on the periodic table. Identical atoms with identical attractions for their shared electron pairs form **nonpolar covalent bonds**. Unlike atoms exert unequal attractions for their shared electrons and form **polar covalent bonds**.

Electronegativity is used to determine the direction of bond polarity which can be indicated in the Lewis structure by replacing the short line for the bond with a modified arrow (⟶) pointed towards the more electronegative atom. For example, nitrogen and hydrogen have electronegativity values of 3.0 and 2.1, respectively. The N—H bond is thus represented as

N ←——→ H with the arrow directed toward the more electronegative nitrogen atom. Then, the Lewis structure can be redrawn with arrows replacing the dashes as shown for $NH_4^+$ and $NH_3$.

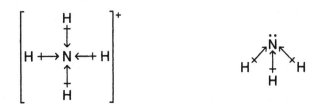

### G. Molecular Dipoles

When there are several polar covalent bonds within a molecule or as a polyatomic ion such as in $NH_3$ and $NH_4^+$ the polar effect of these bonds around a central atom can be cancelled if they are arranged **symmetrically** as shown in $CCl_4$ below. On the other hand, if the arrangement of the polar bonds is asymmetrical, as in the bent water molecule, $H_2O$, the resulting molecule has a definite positive end and oppositely charged negative end, and the molecule is called a dipole. In water, the H atoms have a partial positive charge, $\delta^+$, and the O atom has a partial negative charge, $\delta^-$. The symmetry, or lack of symmetry of molecules and polyatomic ions, can generally be seen in the three-dimensional model.

### PROCEDURE

Follow steps **A–G** for each of the molecules or polyatomic ions listed on the report form. Refer back to the previous discussion, organized into corresponding sections A–G, for help with each step if necessary.

### A. Number of Valence Electrons in a Molecule or Polyatomic Ion

Use a periodic table to determine the number of valence electrons for each group of atoms in the first column of the report form.

    example: $SiF_4$    Si is in Group 4A, it has 4 valence electrons
                           F is in Group 7A, it has 7 valence electrons

    Total valence electrons is 4 + 4(7) = 32 electrons

    If the group is a polyatomic ion, total the electrons as above, then add one electron for each negative charge or subtract one electron for each positive charge.

    example: $CO_3^{2-}$    C is in group 4A, it has 4 valence electrons
                           O is in Group 6A, it has 6 valence electrons
                           Ion has a −2 charge, add 2 electrons

    Total valence electrons is 4 + 3(6) + 2 = 24 electrons

## B.    Lewis Structures for Molecules and Polyatomic Ions

Use the following rules to show the two-dimensional Lewis structure for each molecule or polyatomic ion. Put your structure in the space provided. Use a **_sharp_** pencil with a good eraser and scrap paper. Be as neat as possible.

1. Write down the skeletal arrangement of the atoms and connect them with a single covalent bond (a short line). We want to keep the rules at a minimum for this step, but we also want to avoid arrangements which will later prove incorrect. Useful guidelines are

    a.   carbon is usually a central atom or forms bonds with itself; if carbon is absent, the central atom is usually the least electronegative atom in the group;

    b.   hydrogen, which has only one valence electron, can form only one covalent bond and is never a central atom and does not have lone pairs;

    c.   oxygen atoms are not normally bonded to each other except in peroxides, and oxygen atoms normally have a maximum of two covalent bonds (two single bonds or one double bond).

Using these guidelines, skeletal arrangements for $SiF_4$ and $CO_3^{2-}$ are

$$
\begin{array}{ccc}
& F & \\
& | & \\
F\!-\!&Si&\!-\!F \\
& | & \\
& F &
\end{array}
\qquad\qquad
\begin{array}{ccc}
O\!-\!&C&\!-\!O \\
& | & \\
& O &
\end{array}
$$

2. Subtract two electrons from the total valence electrons for each single bond used in the skeletal arrangement. This calculation gives the net number of electrons available for completing the electron structure. In the examples above, there are 4 and 3 single bonds, respectively. With $2\,e^-$ per bond the calculation is

$$
SiF_4 \text{: } 32\,e^- - 4(2e^-) = 24\,e^- \text{ left to}
$$
be assigned to the molecule
$$
CO_3^{2-} \text{: } 24\,e^- - 3(2e^-) = 18\,e^- \text{ left to}
$$
be assigned to the polyatomic ion

3. Distribute these remaining electrons as pairs of dots around each atom (except hydrogen) to give each atom a total of eight electrons around it. If there are not enough electrons available, move on to step 4.

$$
\begin{array}{ccc}
& :\!\ddot{F}\!: & \\
& | & \\
:\!\ddot{F}\!-\!&Si&\!-\!\ddot{F}\!: \\
& | & \\
& :\!\ddot{F}\!: &
\end{array}
\qquad\qquad
\begin{array}{ccc}
:\!\ddot{O}\!-\!&C&\!-\!\ddot{O}\!: \\
& | & \\
& :\!\ddot{O}\!: &
\end{array}
$$

all atoms have 8 electrons<br>
so the Lewis structure<br>
is complete
        
C does not have an octet of<br>
electrons so it is necessary to<br>
continue on with step 4

4. Check each Lewis structure to determine if every atom except hydrogen has an octet of electrons. If there are not enough electrons to give each of these atoms eight electrons, change single bonds between atoms to double or triple bonds by shifting unshared pairs of electrons as needed. A double bond counts as $4\,e^-$ for each atom to which it is bonded.

For $CO_3^{2-}$, shift 2 e$^-$ from one of the O atoms and place it between C and that O.

$$\left[ :\ddot{O} - C \overset{\frown}{\underset{\underset{\overset{|}{:\ddot{O}:}}{}}{\overset{\cdots}{O}}:} \right]^{2-} \longrightarrow \left[ :\ddot{O} - C = \ddot{O} \atop \quad \underset{:\ddot{O}:}{|} \right]^{2-}$$

Now, all the atoms have 8 e$^-$ around them. (Don't forget the $^{2-}$)

Let's do two more examples.

Example 1: $NH_4^+$     N is in group 5A, it has 5 valence electrons

H is in group 1A, it has 1 valence electron

Ion has a +1 charge, subtract 1 electron

Total valence electrons is $5 + 4(1) - 1 = 8$ electrons

Therefore, the Lewis structure for $NH_4^+$ is 
$$\left[ {H \atop H:\ddot{N}:H \atop H} \right]^+$$

Example 2: $CH_3CCH$ (for this molecule, step 4 has to be done twice to yield one triple bond)

C is in group 4A, it has 4 valence electrons

H is in group 1A, it has 1 valence electron

Total valence electrons is $3(4) + 4(1) = 16$ electrons

The Lewis structure for $CH_3CCH$ is
$$H-\overset{\overset{\displaystyle H}{|}}{\underset{\underset{\displaystyle H}{|}}{C}}-C\equiv C-H$$

## C. Model Building

1. Use the balls and sticks from the kit provided to build a 3-dimensional model of the molecule or polyatomic ion for each Lewis structure in the report form.

   a. Use a ball with 4 holes for the central atom.

   b. Use inflexible sticks for single bonds.

   c. Use two flexible connectors for double bond and three flexible connectors for triple bond.

   d. Use inflexible sticks for lone pairs around the central atom only.

2. **Leave the model together until it is checked by the instructor.** If you have to wait for someone to check your model, start building the next model on the list. If you complete each structure so fast that you run out of components before someone checks your models, work on other parts of the experiment.

## D. Geometry Around the Central Atom

Look at your model from all angles and compare its structure to the description in the discussion (Section D). Then identify the geometry around each central atom from the following list and write the name of the geometric pattern on the report form in column D.

1. tetrahedral

2. trigonal pyramidal

3. trigonal planar

4. bent

5. linear

If a structure has more than one central atom, determine the geometry for each central atom, one at a time. For example, acetic acid ($CH_3COOH$) contains 3 central atoms; they are C, C, and O. The geometry around the central atoms are tetrahedral, trigonal planar and bent, respectively.

## E. Central Bond Angles

Fill in column E with the bond angles between the central atom and all atoms attached to it. Review the discussion (Section E) to find the value of the angles associated with each geometric form. For molecules with more than one central atom, give bond angles for each. For molecules without a central atom and hence no bond angle, write **no central atom**.

## F. Bond Polarity

**Bond polarity** can be determined by looking up the electronegativity values for both atoms in the Electronegativity table. In the F column of the report form, draw the symbols for both atoms involved in a bond and connect them with an arrow pointing toward the more electronegative atom. If there are several identical bonds it is only necessary to draw one. Use the following as examples.

N ⟵+ H                S +⟶ O

## G. Molecular Dipoles

Look at the model and evaluate its symmetry. Decide if the polar bonds within it cancel each other around the central atom resulting in a nonpolar molecule or if they do not cancel one another and result in a dipole. Some examples:

symmetrical
nonpolar

asymmetrical
a dipole

Remember, it is also possible for all the polar bonds within a polyatomic ion to cancel each other so the resultant effect is nonpolar even though the group as a whole has a net charge.

symmetrical
not a dipole

## H. Resonance

This is the shifting of electron pair(s) from their present location one place either left or right; **nothing else** in the structure **changes.** All of the atoms are still connected in exactly the same sequence and exactly the same position in 3-dimensional space. The only change is the position of the double bond or bonds.

In this sequence, only the double bond has moved. **Nothing else has changed.**

For resonance to occur, there must be a double bond and there must be some place for it to move that does not cause any kind of change to the structure.

Carbon dioxide cannot have resonance. There is no place for either double bond to move to that will not change the structure.

Propene does not have resonance, although there is a double bond. Moving it will cause a change in the structure of the molecule.

# EXPERIMENT 8

## Identification of Selected Anions

### MATERIALS

Wash bottle for distilled water, test tubes, test rack, rubber stoppers

### EQUIPMENT

### CHEMICALS

**Liquids:** organic solvent **Solutions:** 0.1 M barium ~~nitrate~~ Chloride [$Ba(NO_3)_2$], freshly prepared chlorine water ($Cl_2$), 6 M nitric acid ($HNO_3$), 0.1 M silver nitrate ($AgNO_3$), 0.1 M sodium bromide (NaBr), 0.1 M sodium carbonate ($Na_2CO_3$), 0.1 M sodium chloride (NaCl), 0.1 M sodium iodide (NaI), 0.1 M sodium phosphate ($Na_3PO_4$), 0.1 M sodium sulfate ($Na_2SO_4$), and an unknown solution.

### SAFETY

Lab coat, chemical splash goggles

### DISCUSSION

The examination of a sample of inorganic material to identify the ions that are present is called **qualitative analysis.** To introduce qualitative analysis, we will analyze for six anions (negatively charged ions). The ions selected for identification are chloride ($Cl^-$), bromide $Br^-$), iodide ($I^-$), sulfate ($SO_4^{2-}$), phosphate ($PO_4^{3-}$) and carbonate ($CO_3^{2-}$).

Qualitative analysis is based on the fact that no two ions behave identically in all of their chemical reactions. Identification depends on appropriate chemical tests coupled with careful observation of such characteristics as solution color, formation and color of precipitates, evolution of gases, etc. Test reactions are selected to identify the ions in the fewest steps possible. In this experiment only one anion is assumed to be present in each sample. If two or more anions must be detected in a single solution, the scheme of analysis can be considerably more complex.

#### Silver Nitrate Test

When solutions of the sodium salts of the six anions are reacted with silver nitrate solution, the following precipitates are formed: AgCl, AgBr, AgI, $Ag_3PO_4$, and $Ag_2CO_3$. $Ag_2SO_4$ is moderately soluble and does not precipitate at the concentrations used in these solutions. When dilute nitric acid is added, the precipitates $Ag_3PO_4$, and $Ag_2CO_3$ dissolve; AgCl, AgBr, and AgI remain undissolved. Acids react with carbonates to form $CO_2(g)$. Look for gas bubbles when nitric acid is added to the silver precipitates.

In some cases a tentative identification of an anion may be made from the silver nitrate test. This identification is based on the color of the precipitate and on whether or not the precipitate is soluble in nitric acid. However, since two or more anions may give similar results, second or third confirmatory tests are necessary for positive identification.

## Barium Nitrate Test

When barium nitrate solution is added to solutions of the sodium salts of the six anions, precipitates of $BaSO_4$, $Ba_3(PO_4)_2$ and $BaCO_3$, are obtained. No precipitate is obtained with $Cl^-$, $Br^-$, or $I^-$.

When dilute nitric acid is added, the precipitates $Ba_3(PO_4)_2$ and $BaCO_3$ dissolve; $BaSO_4$ does not dissolve. Look for $CO_2$ gas bubbles.

## Organic Solvent Test

The silver nitrate test can prove the presence of a halide ion ($Cl^-$, $Br^-$, or $I^-$) because the silver precipitates of the other three anions dissolve in nitric acid. But the colors of the three silver halides do not differ sufficiently to establish which halide ion is present.

Adding chlorine water ($Cl_2$ dissolved in water) to halide salts in solution will oxidize bromide ion to free bromine ($Br_2$) and iodine ion to free iodine ($I_2$). The free halogen may be extracted from the water solution by adding an immiscible organic solvent such as decane and shaking vigorously. The colors of the three halogens in organic solvents are quite different. $Cl_2$ is pale yellow, $Br_2$ is yellow-orange to reddish-brown, and $I_2$ is pink to violet. After adding chlorine water and shaking, a yellow-orange to reddish-brown color in the organic solvent layer indicates that $Br^-$ was present in the original solution; a pink to violet color in the organic solvent layer indicates that $I^-$ was present. However, a pale yellow color does not indicate $Cl^-$, since $Cl_2$ was added as a reagent. But if the silver nitrate test gives a white precipitate that is insoluble in nitric acid, and the organic solvent test shows no $Br^-$ or $I^-$, then you can conclude that $Cl^-$ was present.

Though we have described many of the expected results of these tests, it is necessary to test known solutions to actually see the results of the tests and to develop satisfactory experimental techniques. During this experiment, you will perform these tests on six known anions.

Then, an "unknown" solution, containing one of the six anions, will be analyzed. When the unknown is analyzed, the results should agree in all respects with one of the known anions. If the results do not fully agree with one of the six known ions, either the testing has been poorly done or the unknown does not contain any of the specified ions.

Three different kinds of equations may be used to express the behavior of ions in solution. For example, the reaction of the chloride ion (from sodium chloride) may be written.

1. $NaCl(aq) + AgNO_3(aq) \longrightarrow AgCl(s) + NaNO_3(aq)$

2. $Na^+(aq) + Cl^-(aq) + Ag^+(aq) + NO_3^-(aq) \longrightarrow AgCl(s) + Na^+(aq) + NO_3^-(aq)$

3. $Cl^-(aq) + Ag^+(aq) \longrightarrow AgCl(s)$

Equation (1) is the **formula (un-ionized) equation;** it shows the formulas of the substances in the equation as they are normally written. Equation (2) is the **total ionic equation;** it shows the substances as they occur in solution. Strong electrolytes are written as ions; weak electrolytes, precipitates, and gases are written in their un-ionized or molecular form. Equation (3) is the **net ionic equation;** it includes only those substances or ions in Equation (2) that have undergone a chemical change. Thus $Na^+$ and $NO_3^-$ (sometimes called the "spectator" ions) have not changed and do not appear in the net ionic equation. In both the total ionic and net ionic equations, the atoms and charges must be balanced.

**PROCEDURE**

**Wear department approved chemical splash goggles and lab coat.**

1. Clean seven test tubes and rinse each twice with 3 mL of distilled water. The first six test tubes are for the known solutions that will be tested to demonstrate the expected reactions with each anion. Use a marker to label these tubes as follows: NaCl, NaBr, NaI, $Na_2SO_4$, $Na_3PO_4$ and $Na_2CO_3$. The last tube is for your unknown and should be left empty for now. Arrange these test tubes in order in your test tube rack.

2. Record the unknown number in the top right-hand column of your report form and label the blank tube in the rack with the unknown number.

Pour 1 mL (no more) of each of the six known solutions—one solution per tube—and 1 mL of the corresponding unknown into the unknown tube. Keep the unknown solution for tests B and C.

**NOTE:** You can save considerable time by measuring out 1 mL into the first test tube and using the height of this liquid in the test tube as a guide for measuring out the others.

 Dispose of ALL solutions in the container marked "Chemical waste."

> For each of the following tests that will be performed on known and unknown solutions, there is a corresponding block on the report form where observations should be recorded. If a precipitate forms, record "ppt formed" and include its color. If no precipitate forms, record "no ppt." When dissolving precipitates, record "ppt dissolved" or "ppt did not dissolve." For the organic solvent solubility test, indicate the color of the organic solvent layer.

**A. Silver Nitrate Test**

 Silver nitrate will stain your skin black. If any silver nitrate gets on your hands, wash it off immediately to avoid these stains.

Add about 5 drops of 0.1 M silver nitrate solution to each test tube. Record the results. Now add about 8 drops of 6 M nitric acid to each test tube; stopper and shake well. Record the results.

**B. Barium Nitrate Test**

Wash all seven test tubes and rinse each tube twice with 3 mL of distilled water. Again put about 1 mL of the specified solution into each of the seven test tubes. Add about 5 drops of 0.1 M barium nitrate solution to each test tube and mix. Record the results. Now add 8 drops of 6 M nitric acid to each tube; stopper and shake well. Record the results.

**C. Organic Solvent Test**

Again wash and rinse all seven test tubes. Put about 1 mL of the specified solution into each of the seven test tubes. Now add about 1 mL of organic solvent and about 1 mL of chlorine water to each test tube; stopper and shake well. Record the results.

After completing the three tests, compare the results of the known solutions with your observations for your unknown solution.

**Record the formula of the anion present in each solution on the last line of the report form.**

2. Write the molecular equations for the following double displacement reactions: Use the solubility table in Appendix 2 for reactions that were not observed directly in this experiment.

(a) Sodium bromide and silver nitrate.

(b) Sodium carbonate and silver nitrate.

(c) Sodium arsenate and barium chloride.

(d) Sodium iodide and lead (II) nitrate.

(e) Sodium phosphate and iron (III) bromide.

(f) Sodium phosphate and barium chloride.

(g) Sodium sulfate and barium chloride.

2. Write the molecular equations for the following double displacement reactions: Use the solubility table in Appendix 2 for reactions that were not observed directly in this experiment.

(a) Sodium bromide and silver nitrate.

(b) Sodium carbonate and silver nitrate.

(c) Sodium arsenate and barium chloride.

(d) Sodium iodide and lead (II) nitrate.

(e) Sodium phosphate and iron (III) bromide.

(f) Sodium phosphate and barium chloride.

(g) Sodium sulfate and barium chloride.

# EXPERIMENT 9

## Single Displacement Reactions

*Handwritten annotations:*

compound → new element ↑

$A + BC \longrightarrow AC + B$

↑ element    ↑ new compound

### MATERIALS

Small test tubes, test tube rack, sanding sponge

*Handwritten:* less active

$ex) \boxed{Zn} + \boxed{Cu}Cl_2 \longrightarrow ZnCl_2 + Cu$

↑ more active

### EQUIPMENT

Rule: more active/reactive elemens can displace the less active/reactive element from compound

### CHEMICALS

**Solids:** strips of copper and zinc measuring about 1 x 2 cm

*Handwritten:* $Cu + ZnCl_2 \longrightarrow$ no reaction   $\boxed{Zn > Cu}$

**Solutions:** 0.1 M lead (II) nitrate ($Pb(NO_3)_2$), 0.1 M magnesium sulfate ($MgSO_4$), 0.1M silver nitrate ($AgNO_3$), and 3 M hydrochloric acid (HCl)

### SAFETY

Lab coat, chemical splash goggles

### DISCUSSION

The chemical reactivity of elements varies over an immense range. Some, like sodium and fluorine, are so reactive that they are never found in the free or uncombined state in nature. Others, like xenon and platinum, are nearly inert and can be made to react with other elements only under special conditions.

The **reactivity** of an element is related to its tendency to lose or gain electrons; that is, to be oxidized or reduced. In principle it is possible to arrange nearly all the elements into a single series in order of their reactivities. A series of this kind indicates which free elements are capable of displacing other elements from their compounds. Such a list is known as an **activity** or **electromotive series**. To illustrate the preparation of an activity series, we will experiment with a small group of selected elements and their compounds.

A generalized single displacement reaction is represented by the equation

$$A(s) + BC(aq) \longrightarrow B(s) + AC(aq)$$

Element A is the more active element and replaces element B from the compound BC. But if element B is more active than element A, no reaction will occur.

Let us consider two specific examples, using copper and mercury.

**Example 1.** A few drops of mercury metal are added to a solution of copper(II) chloride ($CuCl_2$).

**Example 2.** A strip of metallic copper is immersed in a solution of mercury(II) chloride ($HgCl_2$).

In Example 1 no change is observed even after the solution has been standing for a prolonged time, and we conclude that there is no reaction. In Example 2 the copper strip is soon coated with metallic mercury, and the solution becomes pale green. From this evidence we conclude that mercury will not displace copper in copper compounds but copper will displace mercury in mercury compounds. Therefore copper is a more reactive metal than mercury and is above mercury in the activity series. In terms of chemical equations these facts may be represented as

**Example 1.** $Hg(l) + CuCl_2(aq) \longrightarrow$ No reaction

**Example 2.** $Cu(s) + HgCl_2(aq) \longrightarrow Hg(l) + CuCl_2(aq)$

The second equation shows that, in terms of oxidation numbers (or charges), the chloride ion remained unchanged, mercury changed from +2 to 0, and copper changed from 0 to +2. The +2 oxidation state of copper is the one normally formed in solution.

Expressed another way, the actual reaction that occurred was the displacement of a mercury ion by a copper atom. This can be expressed more simply in equation form:

$$Cu^0(s) + Hg^{2+}(aq) \longrightarrow Hg^0 + Cu^{2+}(aq)$$

In contrast to double displacement reactions, single displacement reactions involve changes in oxidation numbers and therefore are also classified as **oxidation-reduction reactions**.


## PROCEDURE

**Wear department approved chemical splash goggles and lab coat.**

1. Place six clean small test tubes in a rack and number them 1–6. To each, add about 2 mL of the solutions listed below.

2. Obtain three pieces of zinc and three of copper. Be sure the metal strips are small enough to fit into the test tubes. Clean the copper and zinc strips, at your station, with an abrasive sponge held under running water. Add the metals to the test tubes with the solutions as listed.

Tube 1: silver nitrate + copper strip

Tube 2: lead (II) nitrate + zinc strip

Tube 3: magnesium sulfate + zinc strip

Tube 4: hydrochloric acid + copper strip

Tube 5: hydrochloric acid + zinc strip

Tube 6: lead (II) nitrate + copper strip

3. Observe the contents of each tube carefully and record any evidence of chemical reaction.

Evidence of reaction will be either evolution of a gas (bubbles) or appearance of a metallic deposit on the surface of the metal strip. Metals deposited from a solution are often black or gray (in the case of copper, very dark reddish brown) and bear little resemblance to commercially prepared metals.

With some of the combinations used in these experiments, the reactions may be slow or difficult to detect. If you see no immediate evidence of reaction, set the tube aside and allow it to stand for about 10 minutes, then reexamine it.

4. Pour the solutions and the metal strips into the waste container. Do not allow the metal strips to go into the sink or into the waste bottle.

# EXPERIMENT 10

## Double Displacement Reactions

### MATERIALS

Medicine dropper, test tubes, test tube rack

### EQUIPMENT

### CHEMICALS

**Solid:** calcium carbonate ($CaCO_3$)

**Solutions:** 6 M ammonium hydroxide ($NH_4OH$), 0.1 M ammonium chloride ($NH_4Cl$), 1.0 M calcium chloride ($CaCl_2$), 0.1 M copper (II) sulfate ($CuSO_4$), 6 M hydrochloric acid (HCl), 0.1 M iron (III) chloride ($FeCl_3$), 0.1 M potassium sulfate ($K_2SO_4$), 0.3 M sodium carbonate ($Na_2CO_3$), 0.1 M sodium chloride (NaCl), 10 percent sodium hydroxide (NaOH), 3 M sulfuric acid ($H_2SO_4$), and 0.1 M zinc chloride ($ZnCl_2$).

### SAFETY

Lab coat, chemical splash goggles

### DISCUSSION

Double displacement reactions are among the most common of the simple chemical reactions and are comparatively easy to study.

In each part of this experiment two aqueous solutions, each containing positive and negative ions, will be mixed in a test tube. Consider the hypothetical reaction.

$$AB + CD \longrightarrow AD + CB$$

where AB($aq$) exists as $A^+$ and $B^-$ ions in solution and CD($aq$) exists as $C^+$ and $D^-$ ions in solution. As the ions come in contact with each other, there are six possible combinations that might conceivably cause chemical reaction. Two of these combinations are the meeting of ions of like charge; that is, $A^+ + C^+$ and $B^- + D^-$. But since like charges repel, no reaction will occur. Two other possible combinations are those of the original two compounds; that is, $A^+ + B^-$ and $C^+ + D^-$. Since we originally had a solution containing each of these pairs of ions, they can mutually exist in the same solution; therefore they do not recombine. Thus the two possibilities for chemical reaction are the combination of each of the positive ions with the negative ion of the other compound; that is, $A^+ + D^-$ and $C^+ + B^-$. Let us look at some examples.

**Example 1.** When solutions of sodium chloride and potassium nitrate are mixed, the equation for the double displacement reaction (hypothetical) is

$$NaCl(aq) + KNO_3(aq) \longrightarrow KCl(aq) + NaNO_3(aq)$$

We get the hypothetical products by simply combining each positive ion with the other negative ion. But has there been a reaction? When we do the experiment, we see no evidence of reaction. There is no precipitate formed, no gas evolved, and no obvious temperature change. Thus we must conclude that no reaction occurred. Both hypothetical products are soluble salts, so the ions are still present in solution. We can say that we simply have a solution of four kinds of ions, $Na^+$, $Cl^-$, $K^+$, and $NO_3^-$.

The situation is best expressed by changing the equation to

$$NaCl(aq) + KNO_3(aq) \longrightarrow No\ reaction$$

**Example 2.** When solutions of sodium chloride and silver nitrate are mixed, the equation for the double displacement reaction (hypothetical) is

$$NaCl + AgNO_3 \longrightarrow NaNO_3 + AgCl$$

A white precipitate is produced when these solutions are mixed. This precipitate is definite evidence of a chemical reaction. One of the two products, sodium nitrate ($NaNO_3$) or silver chloride ($AgCl$), is insoluble. Although the precipitate can be identified by further chemical testing, we can instead look at the **Solubility Table in Appendix 2** to find that sodium nitrate is soluble but silver chloride is insoluble. We may then conclude that the precipitate is silver chloride and indicate this in the equation with an ($s$). Thus

$$NaCl(aq) + AgNO_3(aq) \longrightarrow NaNO_3(aq) + AgCl(s)$$

**Example 3.** When solutions of sodium carbonate and hydrochloric acid are mixed, the equation for the double displacement reaction (hypothetical) is

$$Na_2CO_3(aq) + 2\,HCl(aq) \longrightarrow 2\,NaCl(aq) + H_2CO_3(aq)$$

Bubbles of a colorless gas are evolved when these solutions are mixed. Although this gas is evidence of a chemical reaction, neither of the indicated products is a gas. But carbonic acid, $H_2CO_3$, is an unstable compound and readily decomposes into carbon dioxide and water.

$$H_2CO_3(aq) \longrightarrow H_2O(l) + CO_2(g)$$

Therefore, $CO_2$ and $H_2O$ are the products that should be written in the equation. The original equation then becomes

$$Na_2CO_3(aq) + 2\,HCl(aq) \longrightarrow 2\,NaCl(aq) + H_2O(l) + CO_2(g)$$

The evolution of a gas is indicated by a ($g$).

Examples of some other substances that decompose to form gases are sulfurous acid ($H_2SO_3$) and ammonium hydroxide ($NH_4OH$):

$$H_2SO_3(aq) \longrightarrow H_2O(l) + SO_2(g)$$
$$NH_4OH(aq) \longrightarrow H_2O(l) + NH_3(g)$$

**Example 4.** When solutions of sodium hydroxide and hydrochloric acid are mixed, the equation for the double displacement reaction (hypothetical) is

$$NaOH(aq) + HCl(aq) \longrightarrow NaCl(aq) + H_2O(l)$$

The mixture of these solutions produces no visible evidence of reaction, but on touching the test tube we notice that it feels warm. The evolution of heat is evidence of a chemical reaction. **Exam-**

**ple 4** and **Example 1** appear similar because there is no visible evidence of reaction. However, the difference is very important. In **Example 1** all four ions are still uncombined. In **Example 4** the hydrogen ions ($H^+$) and hydroxide ions ($OH^-$) are no longer free in solution but have combined to form water. The reaction of $H^+$ (an acid) and $OH^-$ (a base) is called **neutralization**. The formation of the slightly ionized compound (water) caused the reaction to occur and was the source of the heat liberated.

Water is the most common slightly ionized substance formed in double displacement reactions; other examples are acetic acid ($HC_2H_3O_2$), oxalic acid ($H_2C_2O_4$), and phosphoric acid ($H_3PO_4$).

From the four examples cited we see that a double displacement reaction will occur if at least one of the following classes of substances is formed by the reaction:

1. A precipitate

2. A gas

3. A slightly ionized compound, usually water

## PROCEDURE

**Wear department approved chemical splash goggles and lab coat.**

Each part of the experiment (except No. 12) consists of mixing equal volumes of two solutions in a test tube. Use about a **2 mL sample** of each solution. It is not necessary to measure each volume accurately. Record your observations at the time of mixing. Where there is no visible evidence of reaction, feel each tube, or check with a thermometer, to determine if heat is evolved (exothermic reaction). In each case where a reaction has occurred, complete and balance the equation, properly indicating precipitates and gases. When there is no evidence of reaction, write the words "No reaction" as the right-hand side of the equation.

1. Mix 0.1 M sodium chloride and 0.1 M potassium sulfate solutions.

2. Mix 0.1 M copper (II) sulfate and 0.1 M sodium carbonate solutions.

3. Mix 0.1 M sodium carbonate and 3 M hydrochloric acid solutions.

4. Mix 10 percent sodium hydroxide and 3 M hydrochloric acid solutions.

5. Mix 1.0 M calcium chloride and 3 M sulfuric acid solutions.

6. Mix 6 M ammonium hydroxide and 3 M sulfuric acid solutions.

7. Mix 0.1 M copper (II) sulfate and 0.1 M zinc chloride solutions.

8. Mix 1.0 M sodium carbonate and 0.1 M calcium chloride solutions.

9. Mix 0.1 M copper (II) sulfate and 0.1 M ammonium chloride solutions.

10. Mix 6 M sulfuric acid and 10 percent sodium hydroxide solutions.

11. Mix 0.1 M iron (III) chloride and 6 M ammonium hydroxide solutions.

12. **Fill the bottom of a clean dry test tube with calcium carbonate. Add about 2 mL of 3 M hydrochloric acid.** Observe the results carefully.

 Dispose of all reaction mixtures in the "waste" container inside the hood.

# EXPERIMENT 11

## Quantitative Preparation of Sodium Chloride

### MATERIALS

Ring stand, ring clamp, ceramic wire gauze, Bunsen burner, evaporating dish beaker (250 or 400-mL), lighter, large ring clamp, small ring clamp, beaker tongs, crucible tongs

### EQUIPMENT

Balance (0.01 and 0.0001 g)

### CHEMICALS

**Solid:** Sodium bicarbonate ($NaHCO_3$), **Solution:** 6 M hydrochloric acid (HCl).

### SAFETY

Lab coat, chemical splash goggles

### DISCUSSION

In this experiment you will examine and verify the mole and mass relationships involved in the quantitative preparation of sodium chloride. Sodium bicarbonate is the source of the sodium ion, and hydrochloric acid is the source of chloride ions. The reaction is expressed in the following equation, which shows that sodium bicarbonate and hydrochloric acid react with each other in a 1-to-1-mole ratio:

$$NaHCO_3(aq) + HCl(aq) \longrightarrow NaCl(aq) + H_2O(l) + CO_2(g)$$

Furthermore, for every mole of sodium bicarbonate present, 1 mole of sodium chloride is formed. From these molar relationships we can calculate the amount of sodium chloride that is theoretically obtainable from any specified amount of sodium bicarbonate in the reaction. The experimental value can then be compared to the theoretical value.

To conduct the experiment quantitatively, we need to react all the sodium ion from a known amount of sodium bicarbonate and to isolate the NaCl in pure a form as feasible. To ensure complete reaction of the sodium bicarbonate, an excess of hydrochloric acid is used. The end of the reaction is detectable because the evolution of the gaseous product $CO_2$ stops when all the $NaHCO_3$ has been reacted.

Use the following relationships in your calculations:

1. 1 mole $NaHCO_3$ reacted = 1 mole HCl reacted = 1 mole NaCl produced

2. 1 mole of solute = 1 molar mass of solute

# EXPERIMENT 11

## Quantitative Preparation of Sodium Chloride

### MATERIALS

Ring stand, ring clamp, ceramic wire gauze, Bunsen burner, evaporating dish beaker (250 or 400-mL), lighter, large ring clamp, small ring clamp, beaker tongs, crucible tongs

### EQUIPMENT

Balance (0.01 and 0.0001 g)

### CHEMICALS

**Solid:** Sodium bicarbonate ($NaHCO_3$), **Solution:** 6 M hydrochloric acid (HCl).

### SAFETY

Lab coat, chemical splash goggles

### DISCUSSION

In this experiment you will examine and verify the mole and mass relationships involved in the quantitative preparation of sodium chloride. Sodium bicarbonate is the source of the sodium ion, and hydrochloric acid is the source of chloride ions. The reaction is expressed in the following equation, which shows that sodium bicarbonate and hydrochloric acid react with each other in a 1-to-1-mole ratio:

$$NaHCO_3(aq) + HCl(aq) \longrightarrow NaCl(aq) + H_2O(l) + CO_2(g)$$

Furthermore, for every mole of sodium bicarbonate present, 1 mole of sodium chloride is formed. From these molar relationships we can calculate the amount of sodium chloride that is theoretically obtainable from any specified amount of sodium bicarbonate in the reaction. The experimental value can then be compared to the theoretical value.

To conduct the experiment quantitatively, we need to react all the sodium ion from a known amount of sodium bicarbonate and to isolate the NaCl in pure a form as feasible. To ensure complete reaction of the sodium bicarbonate, an excess of hydrochloric acid is used. The end of the reaction is detectable because the evolution of the gaseous product $CO_2$ stops when all the $NaHCO_3$ has been reacted.

Use the following relationships in your calculations:

1. 1 mole $NaHCO_3$ reacted = 1 mole HCl reacted = 1 mole NaCl produced

2. 1 mole of solute = 1 molar mass of solute

Example:   moles $NaHCO_3$ = $(g\,NaHCO_3)\left(\dfrac{1\,mol\,NaHCO_3}{84.01\,g\,NaHCO_3}\right)$

3. Molarity = $\dfrac{\text{moles solute}}{\text{L solution}}$ and for the HCl used in this reaction we can set up the conversion factors

$$\dfrac{6.0\,mol\,HCl}{1\,L} \quad \text{or} \quad \dfrac{6.0\,mol\,HCl}{1000\,mL}$$

Note that molarity is an expression of concentration, the units of which are *always* moles of solute per liter of solution from which conversions factors for mol $\longleftrightarrow$ volume can be derived. For example, if you wanted to determine the volume of 2.0 M HCl that would be used to complete the reaction with 5.5000 g of $NaHCO_3$, the dimensional analysis setup would be:

$$mL\,HCl = (5.5000\,g\,NaHCO_3)\left(\dfrac{1\,mole\,NaHCO_3}{84.01\,g\,NaHCO_3}\right)\left(\dfrac{1\,mol\,HCl}{1\,mol\,NaHCO_3}\right)\left(\dfrac{1000\,mL}{2.0\,mol\,HCl}\right) = 33\,mL\,HCl$$

4. Percentage error = $\left(\dfrac{\text{theoretical value} - \text{experimental value}}{\text{theoretical value}}\right)(100)$

## PROCEDURE

**Wear department approved chemical splash goggles and lab coat.**

1. Measure masses to the nearest 0.0001 g.

2. Use the same balance for all weighings.

3. Record all data directly on the report form as they are obtained.

1. Weigh a clean, dry evaporating dish to the nearest 0.0001 g.

2. Now add between 2 and 3 g (no more) of sodium bicarbonate to a weighing paper. Transfer all the sodium bicarbonate from the weighing paper to the evaporating dish and reweigh. Record the mass to the nearest 0.0001 g.

3. Dissolve the sodium bicarbonate by adding 5 mL of distilled water and stir gently with a glass stirrer. If all the sodium bicarbonate does not completely dissolve, do not worry about it. Continue on with the next step.

4. In a small graduated cylinder, obtain 6.0 mL of 6 M HCl aqueous solution. Add the HCl solution slowly, with stirring, to the bicarbonate solution in the evaporating dish. (The products are formed in this step). Stir this mixture until the evolution of gaseous product stops.

5. Using a beaker of water to make a water bath as shown in Experiment 1, Part B, evaporate the liquid from the solution. Replenish the water in the water bath as needed. When the water has essentially evaporated from the evaporating dish (the residue in the dish

looks dry), allow the system to cool for a few minutes; remove the evaporating dish and thoroughly dry the bottom of the dish.

6. The following method of drying the product must be followed to avoid spattering and loss of product. Pay attention during this procedure. Do not leave the drying setup unattended.

   Adjust the burner so you have a nonluminous, 10 to 15 cm (4 to 6 in.) flame **without a distinct inner cone**. Place the evaporating dish on a ceramic wire gauze 4–6 inches above the top of the barrel. Heat the dish and contents for 5–10 minutes (the NaCl should appear dry). Touch the surface with a stirring rod to prevent the formation of a crust. If spattering occurs, remove the burner momentarily and either lower the flame or raise the dish before continuing heating.

7. Cool the dish and then record the mass. This is the mass of the product after the first heating. Heat the dish for an additional 5 minutes. Cool again and reweigh. This is the mass of the product after the second heating. If the second weighing is within 0.005 g of the first, the NaCl may be considered dry. If the second weighing has decreased more than 0.005 g, a third heating (5 minutes) and weighing is necessary. The experiment is complete after obtaining constant weight (within 0.005 g). If constant weight is not obtained after three heatings, your instructor will provide instructions on what to do.

8. From the data collected, determine the mass of NaCl produced.

9. Dissolve the NaCl in water and wash it down the sink.

# EXPERIMENT 12

## Properties of Solutions

**MATERIALS**

Ring stand, small ring clamp, crucible tongs, test tubes, test tube rack, beakers, ceramic wire gauze, rubber stoppers, labeled spatulas

**EQUIPMENT**

Balance (0.01g)

**CHEMICALS**

**Solids:** Ammonium chloride ($NH_4Cl$), calcium chloride ($CaCl_2$), calcium sulfate ($CaSO_4$), fine and coarse crystals of sodium chloride (NaCl), and sodium sulfate ($Na_2SO_4$)

**Liquids:** Organic solvent, isopropyl alcohol ($C_3H_7OH$), kerosene

**Solutions:** Saturated iodine-water ($I_2$), saturated potassium chloride (KCl)

**SAFETY**

Lab coat, chemical splash goggles

**DISCUSSION**

**Solute, Solvent, and Solution**

The term **solution** is used in chemistry to describe a homogeneous mixture in which at least one substance (the **solute**) is dissolved in another substance (the **solvent**). The solvent is the substance present in greater quantity and the name of the solution is taken from the name of the solute. Thus, when sodium chloride is dissolved in water, sodium chloride is the solute, water is the solvent, and the solution is called a sodium chloride solution.

In this experiment we will be working with two common types of solutions: those in which a solid solute is dissolved in a liquid solvent (water), and a few in which a liquid solute is dissolved in a liquid solvent.

Like other mixtures, a solution has variable composition, since more or less solute can be dissolved in a given quantity of a solvent. The amount of solute that remains uniformly dispersed throughout the solution after mixing is referred to as the **solution concentration** and can be expressed in many different ways. The maximum concentration that a solution can have varies depending on many factors, including the temperature, the kind of particles in the solute, and interactions between the solute particles and the solvent. In general, water, which is polar, is a better solvent for inorganic than for organic substances. On the other hand, nonpolar solvents such as benzene, organic solvent, and ether are good solvents for many organic substances that are practically insoluble in water.

Dissolved solute particles can be either molecules or ions and their size is of the order of $10^{-8}$ to $10^{-7}$ cm (1-10 Å). Many substances will react chemically with each other only when they are dissociated into ions in solution. For example, when the two solids sodium chloride (NaCl) and silver nitrate ($AgNO_3$) are mixed, no detectable reaction is observed. However, when aqueous solutions of these salts are mixed, their component ions react immediately to form a white precipitate (AgCl).

The rate at which a solute and solvent will form a solution depends on several factors, all of which are related to the amount of contact between the solute particles and the solvent. A solid can dissolve only at the surface that is in contact with the solvent. Any change which increases that contact will increase the rate of solution and vice versa. Thus, the rate of dissolving a solid solute depends on:

1. The particle size of the solute
2. Agitation or stirring of the solution
3. The temperature of the solution
4. The concentration of the solute in solution

## Solubility, Miscibility, and Concentration

The term **solubility** refers to the maximum amount of solute that will dissolve in a specified amount of solvent under stated conditions. At a specific temperature, there is a limit to the amount of solute that will dissolve in a given amount of solvent.

Solubility can be expressed in a relative, qualitative way. For example a solute may be very soluble, moderately soluble, slightly soluble, or insoluble in a given solvent at a given temperature. Table 12.1 shows how temperature effects the amount of four different salts that dissolve in 100.0 g of water.

**Table 12.1**
**Temperature Effect on Solubility of Four Salts in Water, g solute/100.0 g water**

|  | 0°C | 10°C | 20°C | 30°C | 40°C | 50°C | 60°C | 70°C | 80°C | 90°C | 100°C |
|---|---|---|---|---|---|---|---|---|---|---|---|
| **KCl** | 27.6 | 31.0 | 34.0 | 37.0 | 40.0 | 42.6 | 45.5 | 48.3 | 51.1 | 54.0 | 55.6 |
| **NaCl** | 35.7 | 35.8 | 36.0 | 36.3 | 36.6 | 37.0 | 37.3 | 37.8 | 38.4 | 39.0 | 39.8 |
| **KBr** | 53.5 | 59.5 | 65.2 | 70.6 | 75.5 | 80.2 | 85.5 | 90.0 | 95.0 | 99.2 | 104.0 |
| **BaCl$_2$** | 31.6 | 33.3 | 35.7 | 38.2 | 40.7 | 43.6 | 46.6 | 49.4 | 52.6 | 55.7 | 58.8 |

The term **miscibility** describes the solubility of two liquids in each other. When both the solute and solvent are liquids, their solubility in each other is described as miscible (soluble) or immiscible (insoluble). For example, ethyl alcohol and water are miscible; oil and water are immiscible.

The **concentration** of a solution expresses how much solute is dissolved in solution and can be expressed several ways:

1. **Dilute vs. Concentrated:** a dilute solution contains a relatively small amount of solute in a given volume of solution; a concentrated solution contains a relatively large amount of solute per unit volume of solution.

2. **Saturated vs. Unsaturated vs. Supersaturated:**

a. A **saturated** solution contains as much dissolved solute as possible at a given temperature and pressure. The dissolved solute is in equilibrium with undissolved solute. A saturated solution can be dilute or concentrated. The solutions described in Table 12.1 are saturated at each temperature.

$$\text{Solute (solid)} \rightleftharpoons \text{Solute (dissolved)}$$

b. **Unsaturated** solutions contain less solute per unit volume than the corresponding saturated solution. Thus, more solute will dissolve in an unsaturated solution (until saturation is reached).

c. **Supersaturated** solutions contain more dissolved solute than is normally present in the corresponding saturated solution. However, a supersaturated solution is in a very unstable state and will form a saturated solution if disturbed. For example, when a small crystal of the dissolved salt is dropped into a supersaturated solution, crystallization begins at once and salt precipitates until a saturated solution is formed.

3. **Mass-percent Solution** is a quantitative expression of concentration expressed as the percent by mass of the solute in a solution. For example, a 10.0% sodium hydroxide solution contains 10.0 g of NaOH in 100.0 g of solution (10.0 g NaOH + 90.0 g $H_2O$); 2.0 g NaOH in 20.0 g of solution (2.0 g NaOH + 18.0 g $H_2O$). The formula for calculating mass percent is:

$$\text{Mass percent} = \left( \frac{\text{g solute}}{\text{g solute + g solvent}} \right)(100)$$

4. **Mass per 100.0 g solvent** is another quantitative expression of concentration (and the one used in Table 12.1). It is not the same as the Mass percent concentration above because the units are g solute/100.0 g solvent. Thus, for the 10.0% NaOH solution described in No. 3, the g NaOH/100.0 g $H_2O$ would be calculated as follows:

$$\left( \frac{10.0 \text{ g NaOH}}{90.0 \text{ g } H_2O} \right)(100) = \frac{11.0 \text{ g NaOH}}{100.0 \text{ g } H_2O}$$

5. **Molarity** is the most common quantitative expression of concentration. Molarity is the number of moles (molar mass) of solute per liter of solution. Thus a solution containing 1 mole of NaOH (40.00 g) per liter is 1 molar (abbreviated 1 M). The concentration of a solution containing 0.5 mole in 500 mL (0.5 L) is also 1 M. The formula for calculating molarity is:

$$\text{Molarity} = \frac{\text{moles of solute}}{\text{liter of solution}} = \frac{\text{moles}}{\text{liter}}$$

# PROCEDURE

**Wear department approved chemical splash goggles and lab coat.**

## A. Concentration of a Saturated Solution

Use the same balance for all weighings.

1. Prepare a water bath with a 250-mL beaker half full of tap water and heat to boiling. (See Figure 0.3.)

2. Weigh an empty evaporating dish. Obtain 3 mL of saturated potassium chloride solution and pour it into the dish. Weigh the dish with the solution in it and record these masses on the report form.

3. Place the evaporating dish on the beaker of boiling water and continue to boil until the potassium chloride solution has evaporated almost to dryness (about 25 to 30 minutes), adding more water to the beaker as needed.

While the evaporation is proceeding, continue with other parts of the experiment.

4. Remove the evaporating dish and beaker from the wire gauze and dry the bottom of the dish with a towel. Put the dish on the wire gauze and heat gently for 1-2 minutes to evaporate the last traces of water. Do not heat too strongly because at high temperatures there is danger of sample loss by spattering.

5. Allow the dish with dry potassium chloride to cool on the ceramic wire gauze for 5 to 10 minutes and weigh. To be sure that all the water has evaporated from the potassium chloride, put the dish back on the wire gauze and heat gently again for 1-2 minutes.

6. Allow the dish to cool again on the ceramic wire gauze for 5 to 10 minutes and reweigh. The second weighing should be no more than 0.05g less than the first weighing. Otherwise a third heating and weighng should be done.

 7. Add water to the residue in the dish to redissolve the potassium chloride. Pour the solution into the sink and flush generously with water.

## B. Relative Solubility of a Solute in Two Solvents

1. Obtain and clean two test tubes. Label them as test tube 1 and 2, respectively.

2. Add about 1 mL of organic solvent and 3 mL of water to test tube #1, stopper it, and shake gently for about 5 seconds. Allow the liquid layers to separate and note which liquid has the greatest density.

3. Put about 5mL of the $I_{2(aq)}$ in test tube #2. Pour about 1 mL of it into the organic solvent/water test tube (tube #1). Save the rest of this liquid as a control (tube #2). Note the color

of each layer in tube #1, insert a stopper and shake for about 20 seconds. Allow the liquids to separate and compare the color of water layer in tube #1 to the color of the $I_{2(aq)}$ in tube #2.

 4. Dispose of the mixture in this test tube in the waste container in the hood.

## C. Miscibility of Liquids

1. Take three dry test tubes and add liquids to each test tube as follows:

   a. Test tube 1: 1 mL kerosene and 1 mL isopropyl alcohol (2-propanol)

   b. Test tube 2: 1 mL kerosene and 1 mL water

   c. Test tube 3: 1 mL water and 1 mL isopropyl alcohol (2-propanol)

 2. Stopper each tube and mix by shaking for about 5 seconds. Allow the test tubes to stand undisturbed for 1 minute. Record in your data table which pairs are miscible.

Dispose of all the mixtures in the waste container in the hood.

## D. Effect of Particle Size on Rate of Dissolving

1. Add 0.5 g of fine crystals of sodium chloride to a dry clean test tube. Fill another dry test tube to the same mass with coarse sodium chloride crystals. Add 10 mL of tap water to each tube and stopper. Shake both tubes at the same time, noting the number of seconds required to dissolve the salt in each tube. (Don't shake the tubes for more than two minutes.)

 2. Dispose of these solutions in the waste container in the hood.

## E. Effect of Temperature on Rate of Dissolving

1. Weigh two 0.5 g samples of fine sodium chloride crystals.

2. Take a 100-mL and a 150-mL beaker and add 50 mL tap water to each.

3. Heat the water in the 150-mL beaker to boiling and allow it to cool for about 1 minute.

4. Add the 0.5 g samples of salt to each beaker and observe the time necessary for the crystals to dissolve in the hot water (do not stir).

5. As soon as the crystals are dissolved in the hot water, take the beaker containing the hot solution in your hand, slowly tilt it back and forth, and observe the layer of denser salt solution on the bottom. Repeat with the cold-water solution.

 **Dispose of these solutions in the waste container in the hood.**

## F. Solubility versus Temperature; Saturated and Unsaturated Solutions

**Measure the volume of distilled water to the nearest 0.1 mL and masses to the nearest 0.1g.**

1. Obtain two clean dry test tubes. Label the first test tube A (NaCl) and the second B (NH$_4$Cl). See Figure 12.1.

2. Label four weighing papers as follows and weigh the stated amounts onto each one.

a. 1.0 g NaCl      b. 1.4 g NaCl      c. 1.0 g NH$_4$Cl      d. 1.4 g NH$_4$Cl

3. Add the 1.0 g sample of NaCl to test tube A and the 1.0 g sample of NH$_4$Cl to test tube B.

4. Add 5-mL of distilled water to each test tube, stopper and shake for three minutes. Record your observation in the data table.

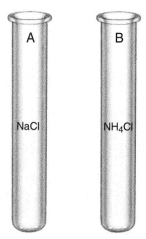

5. Now add 1.4 g NaCl to test tube A and add 1.4 g NH$_4$Cl to test tube B. Stopper and shake both test tubes for about 3 minutes. Note whether all of the crystals have dissolved in both test tubes. Record your observation in the data table.

6. Place both test tubes (**unstoppered**) into a beaker of boiling water; using test tube holder and a glass rod, stir the contents of each test tube, and note the results after about 5 minutes. Record your observation in the data table.

**Figure 12.1**

7. Remove both test tubes from the boiling water bath and place them in a beaker of cold water. Let stand for at least 5 minutes and record what you observe in the data table.

 Dispose of these solutions in the waste container in the hood.

## G. Ionic Reactions in Solution

1. Obtain four clean dry test tubes and label them as indicated below:

Test tube 1: calcium chloride
Test tube 2: ammonium sulfate
Test tube 3: ammonium chloride
Test tube 4: calcium sulfate

2. Fill the bottom of each test tube with the salts respectively as labeled. That is, test tube 1 with calcium chloride, test tube 2 with ammonium sulfate, test tube 3 with ammonium chloride, and test tube 4 with calcium sulfate.

3. Add 5 mL of water to each tube, stopper, and shake for at least 2 minutes. One of the four salts does not dissolve.

4. In a small clean beaker, mix the calcium chloride (test tube 1) and ammonium sulfate (test tube 2) solutions together. Note the results (ammonium chloride and calcium sulfate are the products of this reaction).

 Dispose of all the solutions in the waste container in the hood. You may need to add water to remove most of the undissolved salts into the waste container.

# EXPERIMENT 13

## Ionization–Electrolytes and pH

### MATERIALS

pH paper, wood splints, litmus paper (red or blue)

### EQUIPMENT

Conductivity apparatus; magnetic stirrer and stirring bar

### CHEMICALS

**Instructor Demonstration:**

**Solids:** Sodium chloride (NaCl) and sugar ($C_{12}H_{22}O_{11}$)

**Liquids:** Distilled water and glacial acetic acid ($HC_2H_3O_2$)

**Solutions:** 0.1 M ammonium chloride ($NH_4Cl$), 1 M ammonium hydroxide ($NH_4OH$), 1 M acetic acid ($HC_2H_3O_2$), saturated barium hydroxide [$Ba(OH)_2$], 0.1 M copper (II) sulfate ($CuSO_4$), 1 M hydrochloric acid (HCl), 0.1 M cobalt (II) sulfate ($CoSO_4$), 0.1 M sodium bromide (NaBr), 1 M sodium hydroxide (NaOH), 0.1 M sodium sulfate ($Na_2SO_4$), and 1 M sulfuric acid ($H_2SO_4$)

**Student Activities:**

**Solids:** Magnesium ribbon (Mg), marble chips ($CaCO_3$), sodium bicarbonate ($NaHCO_3$)

**Solutions:** 6 M acetic acid ($HC_2H_3O_2$), 6 M ammonium hydroxide ($NH_4OH$), 6 M hydrochloric acid (HCl), phenolphthalein, 10 percent sodium hydroxide (NaOH), and 3 M sulfuric acid ($H_2SO_4$), 0.001 M HCl, 0.01 M HCl, 0.1 M HCl

### SAFETY

Lab coat, chemical splash goggles

### DISCUSSION

#### A. Electrolytes

Pure water will not conduct an electric current. However, when many solutes are dissolved in water, the resulting aqueous solutions will conduct electricity. These solutes, called **electrolytes**, form ions which are free to move in the solution. The electrical current through the solution is the movement of these ions to the positive and negative electrodes. Electrolytes are **acids, bases, and salts**, depending on the ions in solution. Other substances such as sugar and alcohol dissolve in water but are nonconductors because they do not form ions and are called **nonelectrolytes**.

The ions in an aqueous electrolyte solution are the result of the **dissociation** or **ionization** of compounds in water. Compounds that dissociate or ionize in water are **acids, bases and salts**. For example:

– 113 –

**Dissociation** of NaOH (a base) and NaCl (a salt):

$$NaOH(s) \xrightarrow{H_2O} Na^+(aq) + OH^-(aq)$$

$$NaCl(s) \xrightarrow{H_2O} Na^+(aq) + Cl^-(aq)$$

**Ionization** of HCl (a strong acid) and $HC_2H_3O_2$ (a weak acid)

$$HCl(g) + H_2O(l) \longrightarrow H_3O^+(aq) + Cl^-(aq)$$

$$HC_2H_3O_2(l) + H_2O(l) \rightleftharpoons H_3O^+(aq) + C_2H_3O_2^-(aq)$$

The necessity for water in this ionization process is illustrated by the fact that, when hydrogen chloride is dissolved in benzene, no ions are formed and the solution is a nonconductor (nonelectrolyte).

Electrolytes are classifed as strong or weak depending on the extent to which they exist as ions in solutions. **Strong electrolytes** are essentially 100 percent ionized in water, that is they exist totally as ions in solution. **Weak electrolytes** are considerably less ionized, only a small amount of the dissolved substance exists as ions, the remainder being in the un-ionized or molecular from. Most salts are strong electrolytes; acids and bases occur as both strong and weak electrolytes. Examples are as follows:

| Strong Electrolytes | Weak Electrolytes |
|---|---|
| Most salts | $HC_2H_3O_2$ |
| HCl | $H_2SO_3$ |
| $H_2SO_4$ | $HNO_2$ |
| $HNO_3$ | $H_2CO_3$ |
| NaOH | $H_2S$ |
| KOH | $H_2C_2O_4$ |
| $Ba(OH)_2$ | $H_3PO_4$ |
| $Ca(OH)_2$ | $NH_4OH$ |

In the first part of this experiment, the conductivity of selected aqueous solutions will be demonstrated.

## B. Acids

1. **Acids** are described as substances that yield hydrogen ions ($H^+$) when dissolved in water. This definition was first proposed by the Swedish chemist Arrhenius (over 100 years ago) for electrolytes which share common properties such as sour taste and the ability to change the color of the plant dye, litmus to red. This definition is the simplest way to think of acids and still applies.

Many compounds can be recognized as acids from their written formulas. The ionizable hydrogen atoms, which are responsible for the acidity, are written first, followed by the symbols of the other elements in the formula. Examples are:

| | | | |
|---|---|---|---|
| HCl | Hydrochloric Acid | $H_3PO_4$ | Phosphoric Acid |
| $HNO_3$ | Nitric Acid | $H_2CO_3$ | Carbonic Acid |
| $H_2SO_4$ | Sulfuric Acid | $HNO_3$ | Nitric Acid |
| $HC_2H_3O_2$ | Acetic Acid | $H_2SO_3$ | Sulfurous Acid |
| $(CH_3COOH)$ | | $H_2C_2O_4$ | Oxalic Acid |

Inorganic acids are formed by the reaction of nonmetallic oxides called **acid anhydrides** with water. For example:

$$SO_3(g) + H_2O(l) \rightleftharpoons H_2SO_4(aq)$$

The chemical properties of acids will be observed in Procedure B.

### 2. Bronsted-Lowry Acids and Bases

The more inclusive Bronsted-Lowry acid-base theory defines acids as proton ($H^+$) donors and bases as proton acceptors. Thus, water behaves as both an acid and a base, as illustrated by the equation:

$$\underset{\text{acid}}{H_2O} + \underset{\text{base}}{H_2O} \longrightarrow \underset{\text{acid}}{H_3O^+} + \underset{\text{base}}{OH^-}$$

One water molecule has donated a proton, $H^+$, (acted as an acid) and another water molecule has accepted a proton (acted as a base). The hydronium ion, $H_3O^+$, is a hydrated hydrogen ion ($H^+H_2O$). To simplify writing equations, the formula of the hydronium ion is often abbreviated $H^+$. However, free hydrogen ions do not actually exist in aqueous solutions.


## C.  Bases

The Arrhenius definition for **bases** describes them as substances that yield hydroxide ions ($OH^-$) in water solutions. Bases change the color of litmus to blue. Common bases can be recognized by their formulas as a hydroxide ion ($OH^-$) combined with a metal or other positive ion. Examples are:

| | | | |
|---|---|---|---|
| NaOH | Sodium hydroxide | KOH | Potassium hydroxide |
| Ca(OH)$_2$ | Calcium hydroxide | Mg(OH)$_2$ | Magnesium hydroxide |
| NH$_4$OH | Ammonium hydroxide | | |

The terms **alkali** and **alkaline** solutions are used synonymously with base and basic solutions.

Metal oxides that react with water to form bases are **basic anhydrides**. For example:

$$CaO(s) + H_2O(l) \longrightarrow Ca(OH)_2(aq)$$

The physical and chemical properties of bases will be observed in Procedure C.


## D.  Salts

Salts consist of a positively charged ion ($H^+$ excluded) and a negatively charged ion ($O^{2-}$ and $OH^-$ excluded). Salts may be formed by the reaction of acids and bases, or by replacing the hydrogen atoms in an acid with a metal, or by interaction of two other salts. There are many more salts than acids and bases. For example, for a single acid such as HCl we can produce many chloride salts (e.g. NaCl, KCl, RbCl, CaCl$_2$, NH$_4$Cl, FeCl$_3$, etc.)

The reaction of an acid and a base to form water and a salt is known as **neutralization**. For example:

$$HCl(aq) + NaOH(aq) \longrightarrow H_2O(l) + NaCl(aq)$$

## E.  The Importance and Measurement of H⁺ Ion Concentration

An aqueous solution will be acidic, basic, or neutral, depending on the relative concentrations of $H^+$ and $OH^-$. In acidic solutions the concentration of the $H^+$ ions is greater than that of the $OH^-$ ions. In basic solutions the concentration of the $OH^-$ ions is greater than that of the $H^+$ ions. If the concentrations of $H^+$ and $OH^-$ are equal (as in water), the solution is **neutral**.

There are two general methods for determining the relative concentrations of $H^+$ and $OH^-$ and thus whether a solution is acid, alkaline, or neutral.

1. **Indicators** are organic compounds that change color at a particular hydrogen or hydroxide ion concentration. For example, litmus, a vegetable dye, shows a pink color in acidic solutions and a blue color in alkaline solutions. Another common indicator is phenolphthalein; it is colorless in acid solutions and pink in basic solutions. An indicator can only determine the relative concentrations of $H^+$ and $OH^-$ within the range of its color changes.

A **pH meter** is an instrument designed so that it measures the $H^+$ directly and is used when an accurate measurement of the concentration of $H^+$ is needed.

## F.  Measuring pH

The $H^+$ ion has a great effect on many chemical reactions, including biological processes that sustain life. For example, the $H^+$ concentration of human blood is regulated to very close tolerances. The concentration of this important ion is expressed as pH rather than other concentration expressions such as molarity. The pH is defined by this formula:

$$pH = -\log[H^+]$$

The logarithm (log) of a number is simply the power to which 10 must be raised to give that number. Thus, the log of 0.001 is $-3$ ($0.001 = 10^{-3}$). Since pH is defined as the negative log of an $[H^+]$ value, then the pH of a solution with $[H^+] = 0.001$ moles/liter is $-(-3)$ or pH = 3.

The pH of pure water is 7.0 at 25°C and is said to be neutral, that is, it is neither acidic nor basic because $[H^+]$ and $[OH^-]$ are equal ($10^{-7}$ moles/liter). Solutions that are acidic have pH values less than 7.0. Solution that are basic have pH values greater than 7.0.

| | |
|---|---|
| pH < 7.0 | acid solutions |
| pH = 7.0 | neutral solutions |
| pH > 7.0 | basic (alkaline) solutions |

## PROCEDURE

**Wear department-approved chemical splash goggles and lab coat.**

### A. Conductivity of Solutions—Instructor Demonstration

All of the following tests (except number 7) are performed in 100-mL beakers, using the conductivity apparatus shown in Figure 13.1 or other suitable conductivity apparatus. The electrodes should be rinsed thoroughly with distilled water between the testing of different solutions.

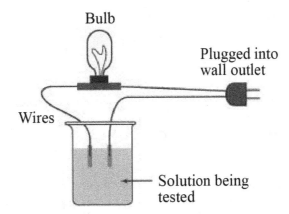

**Figure 13.1  Conductivity apparatus**

Each test is performed by adding about 40 mL of the liquid to be tested to a 100-mL beaker, then raising the beaker up around a pair of electrodes. When a measurable number of ions are in solution, the solution will conduct the electric current and the light will glow. A dimly glowing light indicates a relatively small number of ions in solution; a brightly glowing light indicates a relatively large number of ions in solution.

> **Note:** The student should complete the data table in the report form at the time the demonstration is performed.

1. Test the conductivity of distilled water.

2. Test the conductivity of tap water.

3. Add a small amount of sugar to a beaker containing deionized water. Dissolve the sugar and test the solution for conductivity.

4. Add a small amount of sodium chloride to the same beaker for step 3 and test the solution for conductivity.

⚠ 5. Remove the plug from the electrical outlet, clean and dry the electrodes, and reconnect the plug.

(a) Test the conductivity of glacial acetic acid.

(b) Pour out half of the acid, replace with distilled water, mix, and test the solution for conductivity.

(c) Pour out half of the solution in 5(b), replace with distilled water, mix, and test the solution for conductivity.

6. Strong and weak acids and bases.

(a) Test the following 1 molar solutions for conductivity. Clean and dry the electrodes as needed.
   (i)    Acetic acid
   (ii)   Hydrochloric acid
   (iii)  Ammonium hydroxide
   (iv)   Sodium hydroxide

(b) Test the following 0.1 M salt solutions for conductivity. Clean and dry the electrodes as needed.
   (i)    Sodium sulfate
   (ii)   Sodium bromide
   (iii)  Cobalt (II) sulfate
   (iv)   Copper (II) sulfate
   (v)    Ammonium chloride

7. Clean the electrodes well. Place the 250-mL beaker on a magnetic stirrer. Place about 100 mL of distilled water into the beaker and dip the electrodes into the water. With the stirrer slowly turning, add several drops of the universal indicator to the distilled water. Add several drops (drop wise) of 3 M sulfuric acid in the beaker, until the light bulb glows strongly. Add saturated barium hydroxide solution drop wise until the light goes out completely. Add a few more drops of barium hydroxide solution until the light goes on again.

## B. Properties of Acids and Bases—Student Actives

## I.   Properties of Acids

 Dispose of all solutions in the waste container. Take care to make sure that solids such as metal strips, splints, and unreacted marble chips do not go into the sink. They should be put into the chemical waste container.

### 1. Reaction with a Metal

(a) Into three consecutive test tubes place about 5 mL of 6 M hydrochloric, 3 M sulfuric, and 6 M acetic acids. Test these three solutions with litmus papers, as described in step 2(a), then proceed to part b. (That is, perform experiment 2(a) first, then go back to step 1(b).)

(b) Place a small strip of magnesium ribbon into the first test tube. Immediately invert a clean dry test tube to cover the mouth of the test tube containing the reaction mixture. Wait for at least 30 seconds, then test the gas evolved for hydrogen by bringing a burning splint to the mouth of the inverted tube.

(c) Repeat step (b) for the second acid, then the third acid.

2. **Measurement of Acidity and pH**

   (a) Test solutions of hydrochloric acid, acetic acid, and sulfuric acid by placing a drop of each acid from a stirring rod onto a strip of litmus paper. Note any color changes.

   (b) Place about 5 mL of distilled water into a clean test tube. Add 2 drops of phenolphthalein solution to the test tube. Note the color of the solution. Add several drops of dilute hydrochloric acid, mix, and note any color change.

   (c) Using pH paper to measure the pH of three dilutions of hydrochloric acid in this order: 0.001 M HCl, 0.01 M HCl, and 0.1 M HCl. Record the pH of these solutions.

3. **Reaction with Carbonates and Bicarbonates**

   (a) Cover the bottom of a 150-mL beaker with a small quantity of sodium bicarbonate. Now add about 4 to 5 mL of 6 M hydrochloric acid to the beaker and cover with a glass plate. After about 30 seconds lower a burning splint into the beaker and observe the results.

 Dispose of the reaction mixture in the waste container.

   (b) Repeat the above experiment, using a few granules of marble chips (calcium carbonate) instead of sodium bicarbonate. Allow the reaction to proceed for 2 minutes before testing with the burning splint.

 Dispose of unreacted marble chips in the waste container, not the sink.

4. **Reaction of Acids with Bases—Neutralization**

   (a) Place about 25 mL of water into a beaker, then add 3 drops of phenolphthalein solution and 5 drops of 6 M hydrochloric acid.

   (b) Using a medicine dropper, add 10 percent sodium hydroxide solution dropwise, stirring after each drop, until the indicator in the solution changes color.

   (c) Add 6 M hydrochloric acid, drop by drop, stirring after each drop, until the indicator becomes colorless again.

   (d) Repeat the additions of base and acid one or two more times.

 Dispose of all solutions in the waste container.

## II. Properties of Bases

### Measurement of Alkalinity

1. Make two very dilute solutions by adding 5 drops of 6 M ammonium hydroxide to 10 mL of water in a test tube and 3 drops of 10 percent sodium hydroxide solution to 10 mL of water in another test tube.

    (a) Use glass stirrer, dip a drop of each basic (alkaline) solution you prepared on litmus paper. Note any color changes.

    (b) Add 2 drops of phenolphthalein solution to each of the two alkaline solutions you prepared. Note any color changes.

2. Use pH paper to measure the pH of a diluted sodium hydroxide solution and a diluted ammonium hydroxide solution. Record the pH of these solutions.

 Dispose of all solutions in the waste container.

2. **Measurement of Acidity and pH**

   (a) What is the effect of acids on the color of litmus?

   (b) What color is phenolphthalein in an acid solution?                    _____

   (c) What was the pH of the hydrochloric acid solutions tested?

        0.001 M _____       0.01 M _____       0.1 M _____

3. **Reaction with Carbonates and Bicarbonates**

   (a) What gas is formed in these reactions?

        Name _____       Formula _____

   (b) What happened to the burning splint when it was thrust into the beaker?

   (c) What do you conclude about one of the properties of the gas in the beaker, based on the behavior of the burning splint?

   (d) Complete and balance the equations representing the reactions:

   $NaHCO_3(s) +$      $HCl(aq) \longrightarrow$

   $CaCO_3(s) +$      $HCl(aq) \longrightarrow$

4. **Reaction of Acids with Bases—Neutralization**

   (a) Write an equation for the neutralization reaction of HCl and NaOH.

   (b) How did you know when all the acid was neutralized?

II.  **Properties of Bases**

   **Measurement of Alkalinity**

   1.  What is the effect of bases on the color of litmus?

   2.  What color is phenolphthalein in a basic solution?      _____

   3.  What was the pH for each dilute base tested?

      $NH_4OH(aq)$ _____          $NaOH(aq)$ _____

## ADDITIONAL PROBLEMS

State whether each of the formulas below represents an **acid**, a **base**, a **salt**, an **acid anhydride**, a **basic anhydride**, or **none** of these types of compounds:

$FeCl_3$ _____      $CaSO_4$ _____

$Ba(OH)_2$ _____      $CH_3OH$ _____

$Li_2O$ _____      $C_{12}H_{22}O_{11}$ _____

$HClO$ _____      $HI$ _____

$PbSO_4$ _____      $P_2O_5$ _____

$NH_4OH$ _____      $HCN$ _____

$CaO$ _____      $KOH$ _____

# EXPERIMENT 14

## Neutralization–Titration

### MATERIALS

Buret clamp, wash bottle for distilled water, ring stand, buret clamp, Erlenmeyer flask

### EQUIPMENT

### CHEMICALS

Acid of unknown molarity, standard base solution (NaOH), vinegar, phenolphthalein indicator

### SAFETY

Lab coat, chemical splash goggles

### DISCUSSION

The reaction of an acid and a base to form water and a salt is known as **neutralization**. Hydrochloric acid and sodium hydroxide, for example, react to form sodium chloride and water.

$$HCl(aq) + NaOH(aq) \longrightarrow H_2O(l) + NaCl(aq)$$

The ionic reaction in neutralizations of this type is that of hydrogen (or hydronium) ion reacting with hydroxide ion to form water.

$$H^+(aq) + OH^-(aq) \longrightarrow H_2O(l) \quad \text{or} \quad H_3O^+(aq) + OH^-(aq) \longrightarrow 2\,H_2O(l)$$

A monoprotic acid—i.e., an acid having one ionizable hydrogen atom per molecule—reacts with sodium hydroxide (or any other monohydroxy base) on a 1:1 mole basis. This fact is often utilized in determining the concentrations of solutions of acids by titration.

**Titration** is the process of measuring the volume of one reagent to react with a measured volume or mass of another reagent. In this experiment an acid solution of unknown concentration is titrated with a base solution of known concentration, Phenolphthalein is used as an indicator. This substance is colorless in acid solution, but changes to pink when the solution becomes slightly basic or alkaline. The change of color, caused by a single drop of the base solution in excess over that required to neutralize the acid, marks the **end-point** of the titration.

Molarity (M) is the concentration of a solution expressed in terms of moles of solute per liter of solution.

$$\text{Molarity} = \frac{\text{moles}}{\text{liter}}$$

Thus a solution containing 1.00 mole of solute in 1.00 liter of solution is 1.00 molar (1.00 M). If only 0.155 mole is present in 1.00 liter of solution, it is 0.155 M, etc. To determine the molarity of any quantity it is only necessary to divide the total number of moles of solute present in the solution by the volume (in liters).

To determine the number of moles of solute present in a known volume of solution, multiply the volume in liters by the molarity.

$$\text{Moles} = (\text{liters})(\text{molarity}) = (\text{liters})\left(\frac{\text{moles}}{\text{liter}}\right)$$

For titrations involving monoprotic acids and monohydroxy bases (one hydroxide ion per formula unit), the number of moles of acid is identical to the number of moles of base required to neutralize the acid. In this experiment we measure the volume of base of known molarity required to neutralize a measured volume of acid of unknown molarity. The molarity of the acid can then be calculated.

$$\text{Moles base} = (\text{liters})(\text{molarity}) = (\text{liters base})\left(\frac{\text{moles base}}{\text{liters}}\right)$$

$$\text{Moles acid} = (\text{moles base})\left(\frac{1 \text{ mole acid}}{1 \text{ mole base}}\right)$$

$$\text{Molarity of acid} = \frac{\text{moles acid}}{\text{liters acid}}$$

In order to determine the molarity of an acid solution, it is not actually necessary to know what the acid is—only whether it is monoprotic, diprotic, or triprotic. The calculations in this experiment are based on the assumption that the acid in the unknown is monoprotic.

If the molarity and the formula of the solute are known, the concentration in grams of solute per liter of the solution may be calculated by multiplying by the molar mass.

$$(\text{Molarity})(\text{molar mass}) = \left(\frac{\text{moles}}{\text{liter}}\right)\left(\frac{\text{grams}}{\text{mole}}\right) = \frac{\text{grams}}{\text{liter}}$$

In determining the acid content of commercial vinegar, it is customary to treat the vinegar as a dilute solution of acetic acid, $HC_2H_3O_2$. The acetic acid concentration of the vinegar may be calculated as grams of acetic acid per liter or as percent acid by mass. If the acetic acid content is to be expressed on a mass percent basis, the density of the vinegar must also be known.

## PROCEDURE

**Wear department approved chemical splash goggles and lab coat.**

 Dispose of all solutions in the sink. Flush with water.

**Read all volume to the nearest 0.01 mL.**

## A. Molarity of an Unknown Acid Solution

1. Clean and set up two burettes, one for the acid and the other for the base. See "Use of the Buret" in Laboratory Technique section (page 4) for detailed instructions on cleaning and using the buret.

2. Obtain 160 mL of the base (the standard aqueous NaOH solution) in a clean, dry beaker. Label the beaker "base." On the report form, record the exact molarity of this solution.

3. Rinse one of the burets with two 5-mL portions of the base, running the second rinsing through the buret tip. Discard the rinsings in the sink. Now fill the buret with the base, making sure that the tip is completely filled and contains no air bubbles. Adjust the level of the liquid in the buret so that the bottom of the meniscus is near 0.00-mL. Record the initial buret reading on the report form. Label this buret "base."

4. Obtain 50 mL of the unknown acid in your smallest clean, dry beaker. Label this beaker "acid."

5. Rinse the second buret with two 5-mL portions of the acid, running the second rinsing through the buret tip. Discard the rinsings in the sink. Now add the rest of the unknown acid from the beaker to the buret. Make sure that the tip is completely filled and contains no air bubbles. Record the initial buret reading on the report form. Label this buret "acid."

6. Add approximately 25 mL of deionized water and two drops of phenolphthalein solution into a clean, but not necessarily dry, Erlenmeyer flask. Then add about 10 mL of the acid from your "acid" buret into this flask. Record the final "acid" buret reading in the space provided on the report form.

7. Place the Erlenmeyer flask on a white background, and lower the "base" buret so that the buret tip is inside the flask.

8. Titrate the unknown acid by adding base from the "base" buret until the endpoint is reached. During the titration, swirl the solution in the Erlenmeyer flask with the right hand (if you are right-handed) while manipulating the stopcock with the left. As the base is added, you will observe a pink color caused by localized high base concentration. Near the endpoint, this color flashes throughout the solution, remaining for increasingly longer periods of time. When this occurs, add the base drop by drop until the endpoint is reached, as indicated by the first drop of base, which causes the entire solution to retain a faint pink color for at least 30 seconds. Record the final "base" buret reading.

9. Refill the "base" buret with base, as needed. Note that there is no volume reading after the 50.00 mL mark. Be sure to keep a careful record of all the base added and used.

10. Titrate two additional samples of the unknown acid.

## B. Acetic Acid Content of Vinegar

1. Discard all the solution from the "acid" buret.

2. Obtain 40 mL of vinegar in your smallest clean, dry beaker. Label this beaker "vinegar."

3. Rinse the "acid" buret with two 5 mL portions of vinegar, running the second rinsing

through the buret tip. Discard the rinsings into the sink. Now add the rest of the vinegar from the beaker to the buret. Make sure that the tip is completely filled and contains no air bubbles. Record the initial "acid" buret reading on the report form.

4.  Titrate three 5 mL samples of vinegar using exactly the same procedure outlined in Part A.

5.  When you are finished with all the titrations, empty the burettes and rinse them twice with water.

## REPORT FOR EXPERIMENT 14

## Neutralization–Titration

**Don't forget to write down proper number of significant digits and units.**

### Data and Calculations

**A. Molarity of an Unknown Acid Solution**

1. Write the balanced chemical equation for the neutralization of aqueous HCl with aqueous NaOH.

2. Molarity of the standard aqueous NaOH solution: _____

**Data Table.** Report all volumes to the nearest 0.01 mL.

|  | Trial 1 | | Trial 2 | | Trial 3 | |
|---|---|---|---|---|---|---|
|  | Acid | Base | Acid | Base | Acid | Base |
| Final buret reading |  |  |  |  |  |  |
| Initial buret reading |  |  |  |  |  |  |
| Volume Used (mL) |  |  |  |  |  |  |

**Calculations: Show all work. Use proper significant figures and units.**

| | | Trial 1 | Trial 2 | Trial 3 |
|---|---|---|---|---|
| a. | Volume, in liters, of aqueous NaOH required for neutralization | _____ | _____ | _____ |
| b. | moles of NaOH required for neutralization | _____ | _____ | _____ |
| c. | moles of HCl that were neutralized | _____ | _____ | _____ |
| d. | Volume, in liters, of aqueous HCl that were neutralized | _____ | _____ | _____ |
| e. | molarity of the unknown acid | _____ | _____ | _____ |
| f. | average molarity of the unknown acid | _____ | | |

### B.   Acetic Acid Content of Vinegar

1.  Write the balanced chemical equation for the neutralization of vinegar (aqueous acetic acid, $HC_2H_3O_2$) with aqueous NaOH.

2.  Molarity of the standard aqueous NaOH solution: _____

**Data Table.**  Report all volumes to the nearest 0.01 mL.

|  | Trial 1 | | Trial 2 | | Trial 3 | |
|---|---|---|---|---|---|---|
|  | Acid | Base | Acid | Base | Acid | Base |
| Final buret reading |  |  |  |  |  |  |
| Initial buret reading |  |  |  |  |  |  |
| Volume Used (mL) |  |  |  |  |  |  |

**Calculations:  Show all work.  Use proper significant figures and units.**

|  | | Trial 1 | Trial 2 | Trial 3 |
|---|---|---|---|---|
| a. | Volume, in liters, of aqueous NaOH required for neutralization | _____ | _____ | _____ |
| b. | moles of NaOH required for neutralization | _____ | _____ | _____ |
| c. | moles of acetic acid that were neutralized | _____ | _____ | _____ |
| d. | volume, in liters, of vinegar that were neutralized | _____ | _____ | _____ |
| e. | molarity of the acetic acid in vinegar | _____ | _____ | _____ |
| f. | average molarity of acetic acid in vinegar | | _____ | |
| g. | grams of acetic acid per liter of vinegar *(from average molarity)* | | _____ | |
| h. | mass percent acetic acid in vinegar *(vinegar density = 1.005 g/mL)* | | _____ | |

# Study Aids and Exercises

# STUDY AID I

## Significant Figures

Every measurement that we make has some inherent error due to the limitations of the measuring instrument and the experimenter. The numerical value recorded for a measurement should give some indication of the reliability (precision) of that measurement. In measuring a temperature using a thermometer calibrated at one-degree intervals we can easily read the thermometer to the nearest one degree, but we normally estimate and record the temperature to the nearest tenth of a degree (0.1°C). For example, a temperature falling between 23°C and 24°C might be estimated at 23.4°C. There is some uncertainty about the last digit, 4, but an estimate of it is better information than simply reporting 23°C or 24°C. If we read the thermometer as "exactly" twenty-three degrees, the temperature should be reported as 23.0°C, not 23°C, because 23.0°C indicates our estimate to the nearest 0.1°C. Thus in recording any measurement, we retain one uncertain digit. The digits retained in a physical measurement are said to be significant, and are called **significant figures**.

Some numbers are exact (have no uncertain digits) and therefore have an infinite number of significant figures. Exact numbers occur in simple counting operations, such as 5 bricks, and in defined relationships, such as 100 cm = 1 meter, 24 hours = 1 day, etc. Because of their infinite number of significant figures, exact numbers do not limit or determine the number of significant figures in a calculation.

**Counting Significant Figures.**   Digits other than zero are always significant. Depending on their position in the number, zeros may or may not be significant. There are several possible situations:

1. All zeros between other digits in a number are significant; for example: 3.076, 4002, 790.2. Each of these numbers has four significant figures.

2. Zeros to the left of the first nonzero digit are used to locate the decimal point and are not significant. Thus 0.013 has only two significant figures (1 and 3); The zero is not significant.

3. Zeros to the right of the last nonzero digit, and to the right of the decimal point are significant, for they would not have been included except to express precision. For example, 3.070 has four significant figures; 0.070 has two significant figures.

4. Zeros to the right of the last nonzero digit, but to the left of the decimal, as in the numbers 100, 580, 37000, etc., may not be significant. For example, in 37000 the measurement might be good to the nearest 1000, 100, 10, or 1. There are two conventions which may be used to show the intended precision. If all the zeros are significant, then an expressed decimal may be added, as 580., or 37000. But a better system, and one which is applicable to the case when some but not all of the zeros are significant, is to express the number in exponential notation, including only the significant zeros. Thus for 300, if the zero following 3 is significant, we would write $3.0 \times 10^2$. For 17000, if two zeros are significant, we would write $1.700 \times 10^4$. The number we correctly expressed as 580. can also be expressed as $5.80 \times 10^2$. With exponential notation there is no doubt as to the number of significant figures.

**Addition or Subtraction.** The result of an addition or subtraction should contain no more digits to the right of the decimal point than are in that quantity which has the least number of digits to the right of the decimal point. Perform the operation indicated and then round off the number to the proper significant figure.

Example:
        24.372
        72.21
         6.1488
        102.7308 (102.73)

Since the digit 1 in 72.21 is uncertain, the sum can have no digits beyond this point, so the sum should be rounded off to 102.73.

**Multiplication or Division.** In multiplication or division, the answer can have no more significant figures than the factor with the least number of significant figures. In multiplication or division, the position of the decimal point has nothing to do with the number of significant figures in the answer.

Example: $3.1416 \times 7.5 \times 252 = 5937.624 \ (5.9 \times 10^3)$

The operations of arithmetic supply all the digits shown, but this does not make the answer precise to seven significant figures. Most of these digits are not realistic because of the limited precision of the number 7.5. So the answer must be rounded to two significant figures, 5900 or $5.9 \times 10^3$. It should be emphasized that in rounding-off the number you are not sacrificing precision, since the digits discarded are not really meaningful.

Example: $\dfrac{(27.52)(62.5)}{1.22} = 1409.836 \ (1.41 \times 10^3)$

The answer should contain three (3) significant figures.

# STUDY AID 2

## Preparing and Reading A Graph

A graph is often the most convenient way to present or display a set of data. Various kinds of graphs have been devised, but the most common type uses a set of horizontal and vertical coordinates, $x$ and $y$, to show the relationship between two variables, the independent and dependent variables. The dependent variable is a measurement that changes as a result of changes in the independent variable. The independent variable either changes itself (like time) or is controlled by the experimenter. Usually the independent variable is plotted on the $x$-axis (abscissa) and the dependent variable is plotted on the $y$-axis (ordinate). See Figure S2.1.

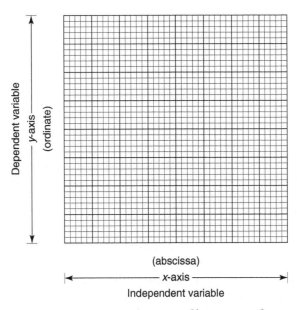

**Figure S2.1   Rectangular coordinate graph paper**

The values for each variable are called data and listed in a data table to facilitate the construction of a graph. As a specific example of how a graph is constructed, let us graph the relationship between the volume of a liquid and its mass. A chemist measured increasing volumes of a liquid and determined the mass of each volume. The data are recorded in Table S2.1. In this study aid, we will use this data to illustrate the steps for making graphs by hand (Part A) and by computer (Part C).

### A.  STEPS IN PREPARING A GRAPH

Most scientists today use computers to help them make graphs from their data. Before we show you how to work with a computer to do this, it is important to learn how to make a graph with pencil, ruler, and graph paper. Use the following step-by-step procedure to plot the data in Table S2.1 on the graph paper provided in Figure S2.2. Your completed graph should resemble the graph in Figure S2.3 very closely. After you complete this first graph, practice your graphing skills by making another graph using the data in Table S2.2 and the grid provided in Figure S2.4.

**PROCEDURE**

1. Examine the graph paper in Figure S2.2 and count how many blocks are available along each axis: This paper has 40 blocks along the x-axis and 40 blocks along the y-axis.

**Table S2.1    Volume vs. Mass Data**

| Volume, mL | Mass, g |
|:----------:|:-------:|
| 21.0 | 19.1 |
| 30.0 | 27.3 |
| 37.5 | 34.1 |
| 44.0 | 40.0 |
| 47.0 | 42.8 |
| 50.0 | 45.5 |

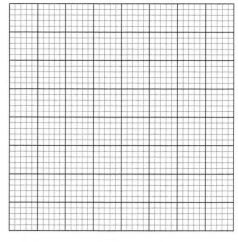

**Figure S2.2    Graph paper sample**

2. Examine the data in Table S2.1 and determine the independent and dependent variables: The amount of liquid in each sample was varied by the experimenter, so volume is the independent variable and will be plotted along the x-axis. The mass of each sample changed as the volume was changed, so mass is the dependent variable and will be plotted along the y-axis. Usually the independent-versus-dependent-variable decision can be reasoned out like this example. If not, then the placement of the variables on the axes can be arbitrary.

3. Determine the range for each variable: The independent variable ranges from 21.0 mL to 50.0 mL. This is a range of 29.0 mL. The dependent variable ranges from 19.1 g to 45.5 g. This is a range of 26.4 g.

4. Determine the scale for each axis; that is, how many units each block will represent. The calculation for the independent variable using this particular piece of graph paper is:

independent variable scale = 29.0 mL/40 blocks = 0.73 mL/block

But, if we adopted this scale, the graph would be extremely awkward to plot and read. So, we round **up** (never round down) this preliminary scale to a more convenient value per block. The most convenient scales to use are generally 0.5, 1, 2, 5, or 10 units per block. The scale is never rounded up to more than double its preliminary value. For this sample data, 0.73 mL/block is rounded up to 1.0 mL/block because it is convenient and less than 1.46 (double 0.73).

Now, we do the same calculations for the dependent variable on the y-axis.

dependent variable scale = 26.4 g/40 blocks = 0.66 g/block. It is not very convenient to count by units of 0.66, so this value is rounded **up** to 1.0 g per block.

5. Determine the starting values for each coordinate: Although it is common for the axes to be numbered starting with zero at the origin (lower left corner), it is not required and some-

times it is a poor choice. For instance, in our example, all of the data for the independent variable are greater than 20.0, so from 0–20, there would be no data plotted. Therefore, we start numbering the $x$-axis at 20.0 mL and the $y$-axis at 15.0 g.

6. Determine the major and minor increments for each axis: We never number every block. Instead we number in major increments of several blocks with minor, unnumbered increments (blocks) in between. Because of our choice of scales, we will label both the $x$-axis and the $y$-axis every 5 blocks. The axes do not have to be numbered every 5 divisions, but often the graph paper has darker lines every five blocks and it is convenient to number at these heavier lines. The numbered increments must be on lines.

7. Label each axis so it is clear what each one represents: In our example, we label the $x$-axis as Volume, mL, and the $y$-axis as Mass, g. Labels and units on the coordinates are absolutely essential.

8. Plot the data points: Here is how a point is located on the graph: Using the 44.0 mL and 40.0 g data as an example, trace a vertical line up from 44.0 mL on the $x$-axis and a horizontal line across from 40.0 g on the $y$-axis and mark the point where the two lines intersect. This process is called plotting. The remaining five points are plotted on the graph in the same way. It is often helpful if each data point is neatly circled so it will be more visible. Then, if more than one set of data is plotted on the same graph, another symbol (an open triangle or square, for example) can be used.

9. Draw a smooth line through the plotted points: In our example, if the six points have been plotted correctly, they lie on a straight line so that a straight edge can be used to draw the smooth line connecting the six points. When plotting data collected in the laboratory, the best smooth line will not necessarily touch each of the plotted points. Thus, some judgment must be exercised in locating the best smooth line, whether it be straight or curved.

10. Title the graph: Every graph should have a title that clearly expresses what the graph represents. Titles may be placed above the graph or on the upper part of the graph. The latter choice, which is illustrated in Figure S2.3, is the most common for student laboratory reports. Of course, the title must be placed so as not to interfere with the plot on the graph. A completed graph of the data in Table S2.1 is shown in Figure S2.3.

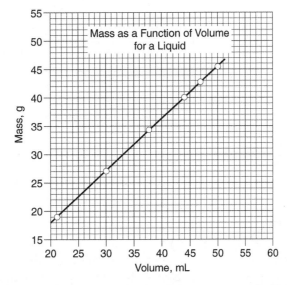

**Figure S2.3   Sample graph of volume vs. mass in Table S2.1**

## Practice Plotting: Sample Data

Table S2.2 is a set of data for you to practice plotting a graph with the steps just described. Use the graph paper in Figure S2.4. Plot °C on the *x*-axis and °F on the *y*-axis.

**Table S2.2
Temperature Scales**

| Temperature, °C | Temperature, °F |
|:---:|:---:|
| 0 | 32 |
| 20 | 68 |
| 37 | 98.6 |
| 50 | 122 |
| 100 | 212 |

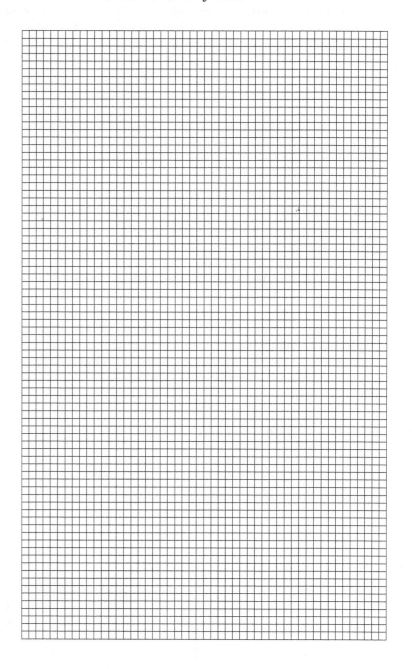

**Figure S2.4    Grid for practice plotting of Table S2.2 temperature data**

## B.    READING A GRAPH

Although graphs are prepared from a limited number of data points (the graph in Figure S2.5 was prepared from six data points), it is possible to extract reliable data for points between the experimental data points and to infer information beyond the range of the plotted data. These skills require that you understand how to read a graph.

**Table S2.3**

| Temperature °C | Solubility, g KClO₃/100 g water |
|---|---|
| 10 | 5.0 |
| 20 | 7.4 |
| 30 | 10.5 |
| 50 | 19.3 |
| 60 | 24.5 |
| 80 | 38.5 |

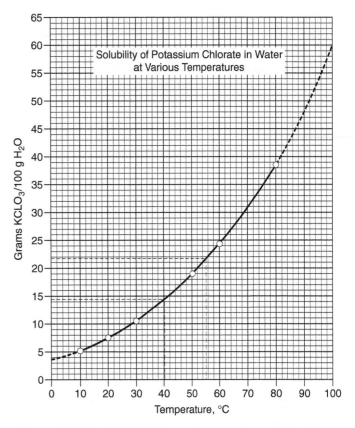

**Figure S2.5  Solubility vs. temperature data from Table S2.3**

Figure S2.5 is a graph showing the solubility of potassium chlorate in water at various temperatures. The solubility curve on this graph was plotted from experimentally determined solubilities at six temperatures shown in Table S2.3.

These experimentally determined solubilities are all located on the smooth curve traced by the solid line portion of the graph. We are therefore confident that the solid line represents a very good approximation of the solubility data for potassium chlorate covering the temperature range from 10°C to 80°C. All points on the plotted curve represent the composition of saturated solutions. Any point below the curve represents an unsaturated solution.

The dashed line portions of the curve are **extrapolations**; that is, they extend the curve above and below the temperature range actually covered by the plotted data. Curves such as this are often extrapolated a short distance beyond the range of the known data although the extrapolated portions may not be highly accurate. Extrapolation is justified only in the absence of more reliable information.

The graph in Figure S2.5 can be used with confidence to obtain the solubility of $KClO_3$ at any temperature between 10°C and 80°C but the solubilities between 0°C and 10°C and between 80°C and 100°C are less reliable. For example, what is the solubility of $KClO_3$ at 40°C, at 55°C, and at 100°C? First, draw a vertical line from each temperature to the plotted solubility curve. Now from each of these points on the curve, draw a horizontal line to the solubility axis and read the corresponding solubility. The values that we read from the graph are

| | |
|---|---|
| 40°C | 14.6 g KClO₃/100 g water |
| 55°C | 21.9 g KClO₃/100 g water |
| 100°C | 59.8 g KClO₃/100 g water |

– 143 –

Of these solubilities, the one corresponding to 55°C is probably the most reliable because experimental points are plotted at 50°C and 60°C. The 40°C solubility value is probably a bit less reliable because the nearest plotted points are at 30°C and 50°C. The 100°C solubility is the least reliable of the three values because it was taken from the extrapolated part of the curve, and the nearest plotted point is 80°C. Actual handbook solubility values are 14.0 g and 57.0 g of $KClO_3$/100 g water at 40°C and 100°C respectively.

# STUDY AID 3

## Using a Scientific Calculator

A calculator is useful for most calculations in this book. You should obtain a scientific calculator; that is, one that has at least the following function keys on its keyboard.

| | | | |
|---|---|---|---|
| Addition $\boxed{+}$ | | Second function $\boxed{\textbf{2nd}}$ or $\boxed{\text{INV}}$ or $\boxed{\text{Shift}}$ | |
| Subtraction $\boxed{-}$ | | Change sign $\boxed{+/-}$ | |
| Multiplication $\boxed{\times}$ | | Exponential number $\boxed{\text{Exp}}$ | |
| Division $\boxed{\div}$ | | Logarithm $\boxed{\text{Log}}$ | |
| Equals $\boxed{=}$ | | Antilogarithm $\boxed{10^x}$ | |
| | | Mode $\boxed{\text{MODE}}$ | |

All calculators do not use the same symbolism for these function keys. Not all calculators work the same way. Save the instruction manual that comes with your calculator. It is very useful for determining how to do special operations on your particular model. Refer to your instruction manual for variations from the function symbols shown above and for the use of other function keys.

Some keys have two functions, upper and lower. In order to use the upper (second) function, the second function key $\boxed{\textbf{2nd}}$ must be pressed in order to activate the desired upper function.

The display area of the calculator shows the numbers entered and often shows more digits in the answer than should be used. The numbers in the display can be in fixed decimal form or in exponential notation, depending on how the calculator is programmed. The MODE key on many calculators is used to change back and forth between fixed decimal and exponential notation. Refer to your instruction manual for how to use this function. Regardless of the digits in the display, the final answer should always be rounded to reflect the proper number of significant figures for the calculations. The calculator will not do that for you.

### Addition and Subtraction

To add numbers:

1. Enter the first number to be added followed by the plus key $\boxed{+}$.

2. Enter the second number to be added followed by the plus key $\boxed{+}$.

3. Repeat Step 2 for each additional number to be added, except the last number.

4. After the last number is entered, press the equal key $\boxed{=}$. You should now have the answer in the display area.

5. When a number is to be subtracted, use the minus key $\boxed{-}$ instead of the plus key.

As an example, to calculate 16.0 + 1.223 + 8.45, enter 16.0 followed by the $\boxed{+}$ key; then enter 1.223 followed by the $\boxed{+}$ key; then enter 8.45 followed by the $\boxed{=}$ key. The display shows 25.673, which is rounded to the answer 25.7.

Examples of Addition and Subtraction

| Calculation | Enter in Sequence | Display | Rounded Answer |
|---|---|---|---|
| a. 12.0 + 16.2 + 122.3 | 12.0$\boxed{+}$16.2$\boxed{+}$122.3$\boxed{=}$ | 150.5 | 150.5 |
| b. 132 − 62 + 141 | 132$\boxed{-}$62$\boxed{+}$141$\boxed{=}$ | 211 | 211 |
| c. 46.23 + 13.2 | 46.23$\boxed{+}$13.2$\boxed{=}$ | 59.43 | 59.4 |
| d. 129.06 + 49.1 − 18.3 | 129.06$\boxed{+}$49.1$\boxed{-}$18.3$\boxed{=}$ | 159.86 | 159.9 |

## Multiplication

To multiply numbers using your calculator

1. Enter the first number to be multiplied followed by the multiplication key $\boxed{\times}$.

2. Enter the second number to be multiplied followed by the multiplication key $\boxed{\times}$.

3. Repeat Step 2 for all other numbers to be multiplied except the last number.

4. Enter the last number to be multiplied followed by the equal key $\boxed{=}$. You now have the answer in the display area. Round off to the proper number of significant figures. As an example, to calculate (3.25)(4.184)(22.2) enter 3.25 followed by the $\boxed{\times}$ key; then enter 4.184 followed by the $\boxed{\times}$ key; then enter 22.2 followed by the $\boxed{=}$ key. The display shows 301.8756, which is rounded to the answer 302.

Examples of Multiplication

| Calculation | Enter in Sequence | Display | Rounded Answer |
|---|---|---|---|
| a. (12)(14)(18) | 12$\boxed{\times}$14$\boxed{\times}$18$\boxed{=}$ | 3024 | $3.0 \times 10^3$ |
| b. (122)(3.4)(60.) | 122$\boxed{\times}$3.4$\boxed{\times}$60.$\boxed{=}$ | 24888 | $2.5 \times 10^4$ |
| c. (0.522)(49.4)(6.33) | 0.522$\boxed{\times}$49.4$\boxed{\times}$6.33$\boxed{=}$ | 163.23044 | 163 |

## Division

To divide numbers using your calculator:

1. Enter the numerator followed by the division key $\boxed{\div}$.

2. Enter the denominator followed by the equal key $\boxed{=}$ to give the answer in the display area. Round off to the proper number of significant figures.

3. If there is more than one denominator, enter each denominator followed by the division key except for the last number, which is followed by the equal key. As an example, to calculate $\frac{126}{12}$, enter 126 followed by the $\boxed{\div}$ key; then enter 12 followed by the $\boxed{=}$ key. The display shows 10.5, which is rounded to the answer 11.

Examples of Division

| | Calculation | Enter in Sequence | Display | Rounded Answer |
|---|---|---|---|---|
| a. | $\frac{142}{25}$ | $142\boxed{\div}25\boxed{=}$ | 5.68 | 5.7 |
| b. | $\frac{0.422}{5.00}$ | $0.422\boxed{\div}5.00\boxed{=}$ | 0.0844 | 0.0844 |
| c. | $\frac{124}{(0.022)(3.00)}$ | $124\boxed{\div}0.022\boxed{\div}3.00\boxed{=}$ | 1878.7878 | $1.9 \times 10^3$ |

## Exponents

In scientific measurements and calculations we often encounter very large and very small numbers. A convenient method of expressing these large and small numbers is by using exponents or powers of 10. A number in exponential form is treated like any other number, that is, it can be added, subtracted, multiplied, or divided.

To enter an exponential number into your calculator first enter the non-exponential part of the number, then press the exponent key $\boxed{\text{Exp}}$, followed by the exponent. For example, to enter $4.94 \times 10^3$, enter 4.94, then press $\boxed{\text{Exp}}$, then press 3. When the exponent of 10 is a minus number, press the Change of Sign key $\boxed{+/-}$ after entering the exponent. For example, to enter $4.94 \times 10^{-3}$, enter in sequence 4.94 $\boxed{\text{Exp}}$ 3 $\boxed{+/-}$. In most calculators the exponent will appear in the display a couple of spaces after the non-exponent part of the number; for example, 4.94   03 or 4.94   −03.

Examples Using Exponential Numbers

| | Calculation | Enter in Sequence | Display | Rounded Answer |
|---|---|---|---|---|
| a. | $(4.94 \times 10^3)(21.4)$ | $4.94\boxed{\text{Exp}}3\boxed{\times}21.4\boxed{=}$ | 105716 | $1.06 \times 10^5$ |
| b. | $(1.42 \times 10^4)(2.88 \times 10^{-5})$ | $1.42\boxed{\text{Exp}}4\boxed{\times}2.88\boxed{\text{Exp}}5\boxed{+/-}\boxed{=}$ | 0.40896 | 0.409 |
| c. | $\frac{8.22 \times 10^{-5}}{5.00 \times 10^7}$ | $8.22\boxed{\text{Exp}}5\boxed{+/-}\boxed{\div}5.00\boxed{\text{Exp}}7\boxed{=}$ | 1.644  −12 | $1.64 \times 10^{-12}$ |

## Logarithms

The logarithm(log) of a number to the base 10 is the power (exponent) to which 10 must be raised to give that number. For example, the log of 100 is 2.0 (log $100 = 10^{2.0}$). The log of 200 is 2.3 (log $200 = 10^{2.3}$). Logarithms are used in chemistry to calculate the pH of an aqueous solution. The answer (log) should contain the same number of significant figures to the right of the decimal as there are significant figures in the original number. Thus the log 100 = 2.0 but the log 100. is 2.000. If your calculator has $\boxed{\text{Log}}$ as a second function you need to press the $\boxed{\text{2nd}}$ key before you press the $\boxed{\text{Log}}$ key.

The log key on many calculators is a second function key. To determine the log using your calculator, enter the number, then press the log key $\boxed{\text{Log}}$. For example to determine the log of 125, enter 125, then press the log key $\boxed{\text{Log}}$. The display shows 2.09691, which is rounded to the answer 2.097.

Examples. Determine the log of the following:

| Calculation | Enter in Sequence | Display | Rounded Answer |
|---|---|---|---|
| a. log 42 | 42 $\boxed{\text{Log}}$ | 1.6232492 | 1.62 |
| b. log $1.62 \times 10^5$ | 1.62 $\boxed{\text{Exp}}$ 5 $\boxed{\text{Log}}$ | 5.209515 | 5.210 |
| c. log $6.4 \times 10^{-6}$ | 6.4 $\boxed{\text{Exp}}$ 6 $\boxed{+/-}$ $\boxed{\text{Log}}$ | −5.19382 | −5.19 |
| d. log 2.5 | 2.5 $\boxed{\text{Log}}$ | 0.39794 | 0.40 |

## Antilogarithms (Inverse Logarithms)

An antilogarithm is the number from which the logarithm has been calculated. It is calculated using the to $\boxed{10^x}$ key on your calculator. Many calculators use the $\boxed{\text{2nd}}$ or $\boxed{\text{INV}}$ or $\boxed{\text{Shift}}$ key to access this function. To use a function that appears above a key you must first press the $\boxed{\text{2nd}}$ key. For example, to determine the antilogarithm of 2.891, enter 2.891 into your calculator, then press the $\boxed{\text{2nd}}$ key followed by the $\boxed{10^x}$ key. The display shows 778.03655, which is rounded to the answer 778. The answer should contain the same number of figures as there are to the right of the decimal in the antilog.

Examples. Determine the antilogarithm of the following:

| Calculation | Enter in Sequence | Display | Rounded Answer |
|---|---|---|---|
| a. antilog 1.628 | 1.628 $\boxed{\text{2nd}}$ $\boxed{10^x}$ | 42.461956 | 42.5 |
| b. antilog 7.086 | 7.086 $\boxed{\text{2nd}}$ $\boxed{10^x}$ | 12189896 | $1.22 \times 10^7$ |
| c. antilog −6.33 | 6.33 $\boxed{+/-}$ $\boxed{\text{2nd}}$ $\boxed{10^x}$ | 4.6773514 −07 | $4.7 \times 10^{-7}$ |

## Additional Practice Problems

Only the problem, the display, and the answers are given.

| Problem | Display | Answer |
|---|---|---|
| 1. $143.5 + 14.02 + 1.202$ | 158.722 | 158.7 |
| 2. $72.06 - 26.92 - 49.66$ | $-4.52$ | $-4.52$ |
| 3. $2.168 + 4.288 - 1.62$ | 4.836 | 4.84 |
| 4. $(12.3)(22.8)(1.235)$ | 346.3434 | 346 |
| 5. $(2.42 \times 10^6)(6.08 \times 10^{-4})(0.623)$ | 916.65728 | 917 |
| 6. $\dfrac{(46.0)(82.3)}{19.2}$ | 197.17708 | 197 |
| 7. $\dfrac{0.0298}{243}$ | 1.2263374  $-04$ | $1.23 \times 10^{-4}$ |
| 8. $\dfrac{(5.4)(298)(760)}{(273)(1042)}$ | 4.2992554 | 4.3 |
| 9. $(6.22 \times 10^6)(1.45 \times 10^3)(9.00)$ | 8.1171  10 | $8.12 \times 10^{10}$ |
| 10. $\dfrac{(1.49 \times 10^6)(1.88 \times 10^6)}{6.02 \times 10^{23}}$ | 4.6531561  $-12$ | $4.65 \times 10^{-12}$ |
| 11. $\log 245$ | 2.389166 | 2.389 |
| 12. $\log 6.5 \times 10^{-6}$ | $-5.1870866$ | $-5.19$ |
| 13. $(\log 24)(\log 34)$ | 2.1137644 | 2.11 |
| 14. antilog 6.34 | 2187761.6 | $2.2 \times 10^6$ |
| 15. antilog $-6.34$ | 4.5708819  $-07$ | $4.6 \times 10^{-7}$ |

# STUDY AID 4

## Dimensional Analysis and Stoichiometry

Chemistry is a quantitative science and involves measurements, complex problem solving. Dimensional analysis is an important tool of chemistry, just calculator, and measuring devices (like the thermometer, buret, and gradua

In dimensional analysis the units for all quantities are always carried al responding number, the units for the answer come out of the calculations a errors in the reasoning behind a series of calculations are easily identified a

Dimensional analysis as a problem-solving tool has many applications in used in many of the laboratory experiments in this manual including: the con into another, calorimetry, solution concentrations, moles and stoichiometry, of reaction. Regardless of the application, the basis of dimensional analysis version factors to organize a series of steps in quest of a specific quantity w

### A.  Conversion Factors

Conversion factors come from equivalent relationships or ratios between two relationships are usually expressed as equations or derived units. When used tors, they are written in fractional form. Some specific examples are shown

| Example Equivalence Statement or Derived Unit | Conversion Factor #1 | Conver |
|---|---|---|
| 1 mole $H_2O$ = 1 molar mass $H_2O$ | $\dfrac{1 \text{ mole } H_2O}{18.01 \text{ g } H_2O}$ | $\dfrac{1}{1}$ |
| 1 atmosphere = 760 mm Hg | $\dfrac{1 \text{ atm}}{760 \text{ mm Hg}}$ | 7 |
| 4.184 J/g°C (Specific heat of water) | $\dfrac{4.184 \text{ J}}{g°C}$ | |
| 8.96 g Cu/1 mL (density of Cu) | $\dfrac{8.96 \text{ g Cu}}{1 \text{ mL}}$ | |
| 22.4 L = 1 mol gas at STP | $\dfrac{22.4 \text{ L}}{1 \text{ mol gas}}$ | |

### B.  Unit Conversions

The dimensional analysis method of converting units involves organizing on sion factors into a logical series that cancels or eliminates all units except tl in the answer

**Problem 1.** What is the volume of a 0.15 lb sample of Cu?

e calculation setup requires two conversion factors: lb $\longrightarrow$ g $\longrightarrow$ mL

$$(0.15\text{ lb Cu})\left(\frac{453.6\text{ g}}{1\text{ lb}}\right)\left(\frac{1\text{ mL}}{8.96\text{ g Cu}}\right) = 7.6\text{ mL Cu}$$

·te, that in completing this calculation, units are treated as numbers, lb in the denominator
· canceled into lb in the numerator and g in the denominator are canceled into g in the
merator.

**Problem 2.** How many grams of sodium chloride are in 0.250 L of a solution with a density of 1.04 g/mL that is 10.0% sodium chloride?

e calculation setup requires three conversion factors:

L $\longrightarrow$ mL $\longrightarrow$ g NaCl(aq) $\longrightarrow$ g NaCl

$$(0.250\text{ L NaCl}(aq)\left(\frac{1000\text{ mL}}{1\text{ L}}\right)\left(\frac{1.04\text{ g}}{1\text{ mL}}\right)\left(\frac{10.0\text{ g NaCl}}{100.0\text{ g NaCl}(aq)}\right) = 26.0\text{ g NaCl}$$

### The Mole and Stoichiometry

is often necessary to calculate the amount of product that can be obtained from a given
iount of reactant or, conversely, to determine how much reactant is required to produce a
ited amount of product. Calculations of this kind, based on balanced chemical equations, are
led **stoichiometry** (from Greek, meaning element measure).

In solving stoichiometric problems, conversion factors based on **the mole** are very important.
its broadest sense a mole is Avogadro's number ($6.022 \times 10^{23}$) of any chemical species. Even
ough the unit "mole" is used as a short expression for molar mass, it is quite permissible to
'er to moles of chemical species that are not really molecular in character. Reference may be
de to moles of such diverse species as sulfur atoms (S), oxygen atoms (O), oxygen molecules
₂), sulfuric acid molecules ($H_2SO_4$), sodium chloride formula units (NaCl), ammonium ions
$H_4^+$), nitrate ions ($NO_3^-$), or even to moles of electrons or protons.

From these definitions of mole we can write two equivalence statements on which to base
iversion factors.

1 mole = $6.022 \times 10^{23}$ items

1 mole = molar mass in g (mass in grams numerically equal to the molar mass)

Three more conversion factors based on the mole are also useful. One applies only to gases:
iole = 22.4 L of gas at STP. The rationale for this is based on Avogadro's famous law that
ual volumes of all gases, at the same temperature and pressure, contain the same number
molecules". The second applies to solutions for which the concentration is expressed as
·larity. Molarity is defined as the number of moles of solute in 1 L of solution. The last is

based on the mole ratios of reactants and products in a balanced equation. For example, in the hypothetical reaction

$$2A + 3B \longrightarrow A_2B_3$$

the mole ratios of the reactants and product to each other are 2 mol A to 3 mol B to 1 mol $A_2B_3$. The following table includes the basic equivalence statements or derived units which include the mole.

| Equivalence Statement | Conversion Factor #1 | Conversion Factor #2 |
|---|---|---|
| 1 mol = $6.022 \times 10^{23}$ items | $\dfrac{1 \text{ mol}}{6.022 \times 10^{23} \text{ items}}$ | $\dfrac{6.022 \times 10^{23} \text{ items}}{1 \text{ mol}}$ |
| 1 mol = molar mass in g | $\dfrac{1 \text{ mol}}{\text{molar mass in g}}$ | $\dfrac{\text{molar mass in g}}{1 \text{ mol}}$ |
| 1 mole = 22.4 L of gas at STP | $\dfrac{1 \text{ mol}}{22.4 \text{ L at STP}}$ | $\dfrac{22.4 \text{ L at STP}}{1 \text{ mol}}$ |
| moles solute/1 L solution | $\dfrac{\text{moles solute}}{1 \text{ L of solution}}$ | $\dfrac{1 \text{ L solution}}{\text{moles solute}}$ |
| moles species A/moles species B | $\dfrac{\text{moles A}}{\text{moles B}}$ | $\dfrac{\text{moles B}}{\text{moles A}}$ |

Using dimensional analysis involving mole conversion factors to solve a problem requires four steps:

1. Write the balanced chemical equation for the reaction involved.

2. Examine the problem statement and determine what is the given substance that will be the starting point for the calculation.

3. Set up a series of conversion factors that eliminate (by cancellation) all units except the unit specified for the answer.

4. Do the calculations and express the answer with the correct number of significant figures.

Apply these steps to the following problems related to the chemical decomposition of potassium chlorate to produce potassium chloride and oxygen.

---

Problem 3.   How many grams of oxygen can be obtained from 15.0 g of $KClO_3$?

---

1. Balanced equation:   $2 KClO_3 \longrightarrow 2 KCl + 3 O_2$

2. The problem states that 15.0 g of $KClO_3$ is being converted to $O_2$. Therefore, the dimensional analysis setup begins with 15.0 g $KClO_3$

3. The calculation setup will be determined by choosing conversion factors that cancel units in the preceding quantity or conversion factor. For this problem, three conversion factors are needed:

$$g\ KClO_3 \longrightarrow mol\ KClO_3 \longrightarrow mol\ O_2 \longrightarrow g\ O_2$$

$$(15.0\ \cancel{g\ KClO_3})\left(\frac{1\ \cancel{mol\ KClO_3}}{122.6\ \cancel{g\ KClO_3}}\right)\left(\frac{3\ \cancel{mol\ O_2}}{2\ \cancel{mol\ KClO_3}}\right)\left(\frac{32.00\ g\ O_2}{1\ \cancel{mol\ O_2}}\right)$$

(Note: 122.6 g and 32.00 g are the molar masses of $KClO_3$ and $O_2$, respectively).

4. Once all the units have been canceled except the units specified for the answer, the calculations can be completed.

$$\frac{(15.0)(3)(32.00)\ g\ O_2}{(122.6)(2)} = \mathbf{5.87\ g\ O_2}$$

---

**Problem 4.** How many oxygen molecules can be obtained from 15.0 g of $KClO_3$?

---

Steps 1, 2 and 4 are exactly the same as in Problem 3, but the last conversion in step 3 requires a different conversion factor:

$$g\ KClO_3 \longrightarrow mol\ KClO_3 \longrightarrow mol\ O_2 \longrightarrow molecules\ O_2$$

$$(15.0\ \cancel{g\ KClO_3})\left(\frac{1\ \cancel{mol\ KClO_3}}{122.6\ \cancel{g\ KClO_3}}\right)\left(\frac{3\ \cancel{mol\ O_2}}{2\ \cancel{mol\ KClO_3}}\right)\left(\frac{6.022 \times 10^{23}\ molecules\ O_2}{1\ \cancel{mol\ O_2}}\right)$$

$$= \mathbf{1.11 \times 10^{23}\ molecules\ O_2}$$

---

**Problem 5.** How many liters of oxygen gas, measured at STP, can be obtained from 15.0 g of $KClO_3$?

---

Steps 1, 2, and 4 are exactly the same as in Problems 3 and 4, but the last conversion in step 3 requires a different conversion factor:

$$g\ KClO_3 \longrightarrow mol\ KClO_3 \longrightarrow mol\ O_2 \longrightarrow L\ O_2$$

$$(15.0\ \cancel{g\ KClO_3})\left(\frac{1\ \cancel{mol\ KClO_3}}{122.6\ \cancel{g\ KClO_3}}\right)\left(\frac{3\ \cancel{mol\ O_2}}{2\ \cancel{mol\ KClO_3}}\right)\left(\frac{22.4\ L}{1\ \cancel{mol\ O_2}}\right) = \mathbf{4.11\ L}$$

---

**Problem 6.** How many grams of $KClO_3$ must be decomposed to produce 25.0 g of KCl?

---

Step 1. Balance the equation for the reaction as shown in Problem 1.

Step 2. Consider KCl to be the given substance; convert to g $KClO_3$ using a sequence of conversion factors.

$$g\ KCl \longrightarrow mol\ KCl \longrightarrow mol\ KClO_3 \longrightarrow g\ KClO_3$$

Steps 3 and 4.   Choose conversion factors to cancel units of the preceding fractions in the sequence.

$$(25.0 \, \text{g KCl}) \left( \frac{1 \, \text{mol KCl}}{74.55 \, \text{g KCl}} \right) \left( \frac{2 \, \text{mol KClO}_3}{2 \, \text{mol KCl}} \right) \left( \frac{122.6 \, \text{g KClO}_3}{1 \, \text{mol KClO}_3} \right) = \textbf{41.1 g KClO}_3$$

---

**Problem 7.**   How many mL of 6.0 M HCl(*aq*) are needed to react with 4.85 g of NaHCO$_3$?

---

Step 1.   The balanced equation for this reaction is

$$NaHCO_3 + HCl \longrightarrow NaCl + H_2O + CO_2$$

Step 2.   Consider NaHCO$_3$ to be the given substance; convert to mL of 6.0 M HCl using a sequence of conversion factors.

$$\text{g NaHCO}_3 \longrightarrow \text{mol NaHCO}_3 \longrightarrow \text{mol HCl} \longrightarrow \text{L HCl} \longrightarrow \text{mL HCl}$$

Steps 3 and 4.   Choose conversion factors to cancel units of the preceding factors in the sequence.

$$(4.85 \, \text{g NaHCO}_3) \left( \frac{1 \, \text{mol NaHCO}_3}{84.01 \, \text{g NaHCO}_3} \right) \left( \frac{1 \, \text{mol HCl}}{1 \, \text{mol NaHCO}_3} \right) \left( \frac{1 \, \text{L}}{6.0 \, \text{mol HCl}} \right) \left( \frac{1000 \, \text{mL}}{1 \, \text{L}} \right)$$

$$= \textbf{9.6 mL HCl}$$

## EXERCISE 1

# Significant Figures and Exponential Notation

1. How many significant figures are in each of the following numbers?

(a) 7.42 _____ (b) 4.6 _____ (c) 3.40 _____ (d) 26,000 _____

(e) 0.088 _____ (f) 0.0034 _____ (g) 0.0230 _____ (h) 0.3080 _____

2. Write each of the following numbers in proper exponential notation:

(a) 423                                            (a) _____

(b) 0.032                                     (b) _____

(c) 8,300                                     (c) _____

(d) 302.0                                     (d) _____

(e) 12,400,000                            (e) _____

(f) 0.0007                                   (f) _____

3. How many significant figures should be in the answer to each of the following calculations?

(a) 17.10           (b) 57.826                    (a) _____

    + 0.77              − 9.4                      (b) _____

(c) $12.4 \times 2.82 =$     (d) $6.4 \times 3.1416 =$      (c) _____

                                                   (d) _____

(e) $\dfrac{0.5172}{0.2742} =$     (f) $\dfrac{0.0172}{4.36} =$      (e) _____

                                                   (f) _____

(g) $\dfrac{5.82 \times 760. \times 425}{723 \times 273} =$   (h) $\dfrac{0.92 \times 454 \times 5.620}{22.4} =$    (g) _____

                                                   (h) _____

4. For each of these problems, complete the answer with a 10 raised to the proper power. Note that each answer is expressed to the correct number of significant figures.

(a) $2.71 \times 10^4 \times 2.0 \times 10^2 = 5.4 \times$ _____       (a) _____

(b) $\dfrac{4.523 \times 10^4}{2.71 \times 10^2} = 1.67 \times$ _____       (b) _____

(c) $4.8 \times 10^4 \times 3.5 \times 10^4 = 1.7 \times$ _____       (c) _____

(d) $\dfrac{1.64 \times 10^{-4}}{1.2 \times 10^2} = 1.4 \times$ _____       (d) _____

(e) $\dfrac{4.70 \times 10^2}{8.42 \times 10^5} = 5.58 \times$ _____       (e) _____

5. Solve each of the following problems, expressing each answer to the proper number of significant figures. Use exponential notation for (c), (d), and (e).

(a)     1.842           (b)  714.3
         45.21               $-\ 28.52$        (a) _____
     $+\ 37.55$

                                                   (b) _____

(c) $2.83 \times 10^3 \times 7.55 \times 10^7 =$             (c) _____

(d) $4.4 \times 5{,}280 =$                         (d) _____

(e) $\dfrac{7.07 \times 10^{-4} \times 6.51 \times 10^{-2}}{2.92 \times 10^4} =$     (e) _____

**Answers**

1. (a) 3, (b) 2, (c) 3, (d) 2, (e) 2, (f) 2, (g) 3, (h) 4.

2. (a) $4.23 \times 10^2$, (b) $3.2 \times 10^{-2}$, (c) $8.3 \times 10^3$, (d) $3.020 \times 10^2$, (e) $1.24 \times 10^7$, (f) $7 \times 10^{-4}$.

3. (a) 4, (b) 3, (c) 3, (d) 2, (e) 4, (f) 3, (g) 3, (h) 2.

4. (a) $10^6$, (b) $10^2$, (c) $10^9$, (d) $10^{-6}$, (e) $10^{-4}$.

5. (a) 84.60, (b) 685.8, (c) $2.14 \times 10^{11}$, (d) $2.3 \times 10^4$, (e) $1.58 \times 10^{-9}$.

# EXERCISE 2

## Measurements

For each of the following problems, show your calculation setup. In both your setup and answer, show units and follow the rules of significant figures. See Experiment 2 and the appendixes for any needed formulas or conversion factors.

1. Convert 78°C to degrees Fahrenheit.

_____

2. Convert −13°C to degrees Fahrenheit.

_____

3. An object weighs 58.62 lbs. What is the mass in grams?

_____

4. A stick is 12.0 inches long. What is the length in centimeters?

_____

5. The water in a flask measures 423 mL. How many quarts is this?

_____

6. A piece of lumber measures 53.62 cm long. What is its length in:

(a) Millimeters?

_____

(b) Feet?

_____

7. A block is found to have a volume of 35.3 cm$^3$. Its mass is 65.32 g. Calculate the density of the block.

_____

8. A graduated cylinder was filled to 25.0 mL with liquid. A solid object weighing 73.5 g was immersed in the liquid, raising the liquid level to 43.9 mL. Calculate the density of the solid object.

_____

9. The density of the liquid in Problem 8 is 0.896 g/mL. What is the mass of the liquid in the graduated cylinder.

_____

10. How many joules of heat are absorbed by 350.0 g of water when its temperature increases from 20.0°C to 80.0°C? (sp. ht. water = 1.00 cal/g°C)

_____

11. A beaker contains 85.32 mL of water. The density of the water is 1.00 g/mL. Calculate:

(a) The volume of the water in liters.

_____

(b) The mass of the water in grams.

_____

12. The density of carbon tetrachloride, $CCl_4$, is 1.59 g/mL. Calculate the volume of 100.0 g of $CCl_4$.

_____

# EXERCISE 3

## Names and Formulas 1

Give the names of the following compounds:

1. NaCl _____

2. $AgNO_3$ _____

3. $BaCrO_4$ _____

4. $Ca(OH)_2$ _____

5. $ZnCO_3$ _____

6. $Na_2SO_4$ _____

7. $Al_2O_3$ _____

8. $CdBr_2$ _____

9. $KNO_2$ _____

10. $Fe(NO_3)_3$ _____

11. $(NH_4)_3PO_4$ _____

12. $KClO_3$ _____

13. MgS _____

14. $Cu_2C_2O_4$ _____

15. LiOH _____

Give the formulas of the following compounds:

1.  Barium chloride                    1. _____

2.  Zinc fluoride                      2. _____

3.  Lead(II) iodide                    3. _____

4.  Ammonium hydroxide                 4. _____

5.  Potassium chromate                 5. _____

6.  Bismuth(III) chloride              6. _____

7.  Magnesium perchlorate              7. _____

8.  Copper(II) sulfate                 8. _____

9.  Iron(III) chloride                 9. _____

10. Calcium cyanide                    10. _____

11. Copper(I) sulfide                  11. _____

12. Silver carbonate                   12. _____

13. Cadmium hypochlorite               13. _____

14. Sodium bicarbonate                 14. _____

15. Aluminum acetate                   15. _____

16. Nickel(II) phosphate               16. _____

17. Sodium sulfite                     17. _____

18. Tin(IV) oxide                      18. _____

# EXERCISE 4

## Names and Formulas II

Give the names of the following compounds:

1. $(NH_4)_2S$ _____

2. $NiF_2$ _____

3. $Sb(ClO_3)_3$ _____

4. $HgCl_2$ _____

5. $H_2SO_4(aq)$ _____

6. $CrBr_3$ _____

7. $Cu_2CO_3$ _____

8. $K_2Cr_2O_7$ _____

9. $FeSO_4$ _____

10. $AgC_2H_3O_2$ _____

11. $HCl$ _____

12. $HCl(aq)$ _____

13. $KBrO_3$ _____

14. $Cd(ClO_2)_2$ _____

15. $HIO_{2(aq)}$ _____

Give the formulas of the following compounds:

1. Sodium oxalate      1. _____

2. Manganese(II) iodate      2. _____

3. Zinc nitrite      3. _____

4. Potassium permanganate      4. _____

5. Titanium(IV) bromide      5. _____

6. Sodium arsenate      6. _____

7. Manganese(IV) sulfide      7. _____

8. Bismuth(III) arsenate      8. _____

9. Sodium peroxide      9. _____

10. Magnesium bicarbonate      10. _____

11. Lead(II) acetate      11. _____

12. Phosphoric acid      12. _____

13. Nitric acid      13. _____

14. Acetic acid      14. _____

15. Arsenic(III) iodide      15. _____

16. Ammonium thiocyanate      16. _____

17. Chromium (III) chlorite      17. _____

18. Tin (II) fluoride      18. _____

# EXERCISE 5

## Names and Formulas III

Give the names of the following compounds:

1. $CO_2$ _____

2. $H_2O_2$ _____

3. $Ni(MnO_4)_2$ _____

4. $Co_3(AsO_4)_2$ _____

5. KCN _____

6. $Sb_2O_5$ _____

7. $BaH_2$ _____

8. $NaHSO_3$ _____

9. $As(NO_2)_5$ _____

10. KSCN _____

11. $Ag_2CO_3$ _____

12. $CrF_3$ _____

13. $SnS_2$ _____

14. $H_2SO_3(aq)$ _____

15. $HgC_2O_4$ _____

16. $Pb(HCO_3)_2$ _____

17. $Cu(OH)_2$ _____

Give the formulas of the following substances:

1. Ammonium hydrogen carbonate          1. _____

2. Hydrogen sulfide          2. _____

3. Barium hydroxide          3. _____

4. Carbon tetrachloride          4. _____

5. Nickel(II) perchlorate          5. _____

6. Lead(II) nitrate          6. _____

7. Sulfur dioxide          7. _____

8. Carbonic acid          8. _____

9. Copper(I) carbonate          9. _____

10. Calcium cyanide          10. _____

11. Aluminum oxide          11. _____

12. Silver dichromate          12. _____

13. Nitrous acid          13. _____

14. Copper(II) bromide          14. _____

15. Ammonia          15. _____

16. Chlorine          16. _____

17. Chromium(III) sulfite          17. _____

18. Bromic acid          18. _____

19. Barium arsenate          19. _____

20. Manganese(IV) chloride          20. _____

21. Carbon disulfide          21. _____

22. Cobalt (II) fluoride          22. _____

# EXERCISE 6

## Equation Writing and Balancing I

Balance the following equations:

1.　　$Mg + O_2 \xrightarrow{\Delta} MgO$

2.　　$KClO_3 \xrightarrow{\Delta} KCl + O_2$

3.　　$Fe + O_2 \xrightarrow{\Delta} Fe_3O_4$

4.　　$Mg + HCl \longrightarrow MgCl_2 + H_2$

5.　　$Na + H_2O \longrightarrow NaOH + H_2$

Beneath each word equation write the formula equation and balance it. Remember that oxygen and hydrogen are diatomic molecules.

1. Sulfur + Oxygen $\xrightarrow{\Delta}$ Sulfur dioxide

2. Zinc + Sulfuric acid $\longrightarrow$ Zinc sulfate + Hydrogen

3. Carbon + Oxygen $\xrightarrow{\Delta}$ Carbon dioxide

4. Hydrogen + Oxygen $\xrightarrow{\Delta}$ Water

5. Aluminum + Hydrochloric acid $\longrightarrow$ Aluminum chloride + Hydrogen

Balance the following equations:

1.    $N_2 +$    $H_2 \xrightarrow{\Delta}$    $NH_3$

2.    $CoCl_2 \cdot 6\,H_2O \xrightarrow{\Delta}$    $CoCl_2 +$    $H_2O$

3.    $Fe +$    $H_2O \xrightarrow{\Delta}$    $Fe_3O_4 +$    $H_2$

4.    $F_2 +$    $H_2O \xrightarrow{\Delta}$    $HF +$    $O_2$

5.    $Pb(NO_3)_2 \xrightarrow{\Delta}$    $PbO +$    $NO +$    $O_2$

Beneath each word equation write and balance the formula equation. Oxygen, hydrogen, and bromine are diatomic molecules

1. Aluminum + Oxygen $\xrightarrow{\Delta}$ Aluminum oxide

2. Potassium + Water $\longrightarrow$ Potassium hydroxide + Hydrogen

3. Arsenic(III) oxide + Hydrochloric acid $\longrightarrow$ Arsenic(III) chloride + Water

4. Phosphorus + Bromine $\longrightarrow$ Phosphorus tribromide

5. Sodium bicarbonate + Nitric acid $\longrightarrow$ Sodium nitrate + Water + Carbon dioxide

# EXERCISE 7

## Equation Writing and Balancing II

Complete and balance the following double displacement reaction equations (assume all reactions will go):

1.    $NaCl +$    $AgNO_3 \longrightarrow$

2.    $BaCl_2 +$    $H_2SO_4 \longrightarrow$

3.    $NaOH +$    $HCl \longrightarrow$

4.    $Na_2CO_3 +$    $HCl \longrightarrow$

5.    $H_2SO_4 +$    $NH_4OH \longrightarrow$

6.    $FeCl_3 +$    $NH_4OH \longrightarrow$

7.    $Na_2SO_3 +$    $HCl \longrightarrow$

8.    $K_2CrO_4 +$    $Pb(NO_3)_2 \longrightarrow$

9.    $NaC_2H_3O_2 +$    $HCl \longrightarrow$

10.   $NaOH +$    $NH_4NO_3 \longrightarrow$

11.   $BiCl_3 +$    $H_2S \longrightarrow$

12.   $K_2C_2O_4 +$    $HCl \longrightarrow$

13.   $H_3PO_4 +$    $Ca(OH)_2 \longrightarrow$

14.   $(NH_4)_2CO_3 +$    $HNO_3 \longrightarrow$

15.   $K_2CO_3 +$    $NiBr_2 \longrightarrow$

Complete and balance the following equations. (Combination, 1–4; Decomposition, 5–8; Single displacement, 9–12; Double displacement, 13–16.)

1.　　$K +$　　$Cl_2 \longrightarrow$

2.　　$Zn +$　　$O_2 \longrightarrow$

3.　　$BaO +$　　$H_2O \longrightarrow$

4.　　$SO_3 +$　　$H_2O \longrightarrow$

5.　　$MgCO_3 \xrightarrow{\Delta}$

6.　　$NH_4OH \xrightarrow{\Delta}$

7.　　$Mn(ClO_3)_2 \xrightarrow{\Delta}$

8.　　$HgO \xrightarrow{\Delta}$

9.　　$Ni +$　　$HCl \longrightarrow$

10.　　$Pb +$　　$AgNO_3 \longrightarrow$

11.　　$Cl_2 +$　　$NaI \longrightarrow$

12.　　$Al +$　　$CuSO_4 \longrightarrow$

13.　　$KOH +$　　$H_3PO_4 \longrightarrow$

14.　　$Na_2C_2O_4 +$　　$CaCl_2 \longrightarrow$

15.　　$(NH_4)_2SO_4 +$　　$KOH \longrightarrow$

16.　　$ZnCl_2 +$　　$(NH_4)_2S \longrightarrow$

# EXERCISE 8

## Equation Writing and Balancing III

For each of the following situations, write and balance the formula equation for the reaction that occurs.

1. A strip of zinc is dropped into a test tube of hydrochloric acid.


2. Hydrogen peroxide decomposes in the presence of manganese dioxide.


3. Copper(II) sulfate pentahydrate is heated to drive off the water of hydration.


4. A piece of sodium is dropped into a beaker of water.


5. A piece of limestone (calcium carbonate) is heated in a Bunsen burner flame.


6. A piece of zinc is dropped into a solution of silver nitrate.


7. Hydrochloric acid is added to a sodium carbonate solution.


8. Potassium chlorate is heated in the presence of manganese dioxide.


9. Hydrogen gas is burned in air.


10. Sulfuric acid solution is reacted with sodium hydroxide solution.

# EXERCISE 9

# Graphical Representation of Data

**A. From the figure at the right, read values for the following:**

1. The vapor pressure of ethyl ether at 20°C.

   _____

2. The temperature at which ethyl chloride has a vapor pressure of 620 torr.

   _____

3. The temperature at which ethyl alcohol has the pressure that ethyl chloride has at 2°C.

   _____

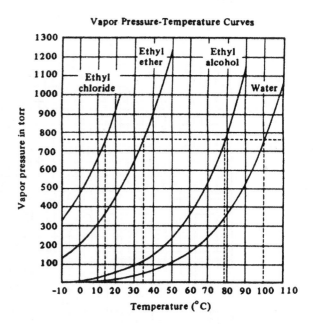

**Vapor Pressure-Temperature Curves**

**B. Plotting Graphs**

1. Plot the following pressure-temperature data for a gas on the graph below. Draw the best possible straight line through the data. Provide temperature and pressure scales.

| Temperature, °C | 0 | 20 | 40 | 60 | 80 | 100 |
|---|---|---|---|---|---|---|
| Pressure, torr | 586 | 628 | 655 | 720 | 757 | 800 |

**Pressure-Temperature Data for a Gas**

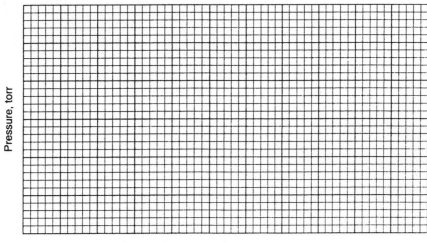

Temperature, °C

2. (a) Study the data given below; (b) determine suitable scales for pressure and for volume and mark these scales on the graph; (c) plot eight points on the graph; (d) draw the best possible line through these points; (e) place a suitable title at the top of the graph.

Pressure-volume data for a gas

| Volume, mL | 10.70 | 7.64 | 5.57 | 4.56 | 3.52 | 2.97 | 2.43 | 2.01 |
|---|---|---|---|---|---|---|---|---|
| Pressure, torr | 250 | 350 | 480 | 600 | 760 | 900 | 1100 | 1330 |

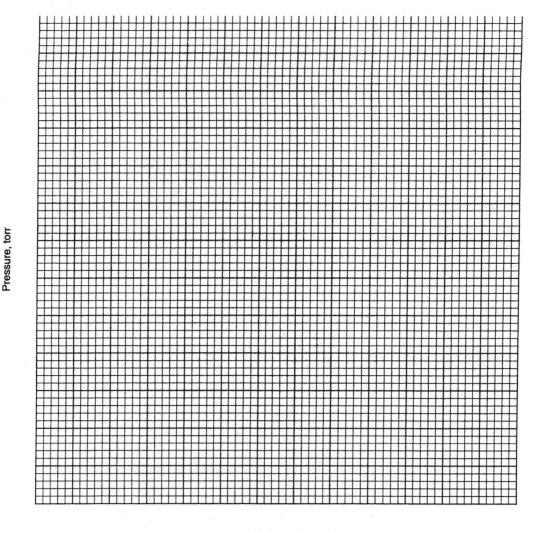

Pressure, torr

Volume, mL

Read from your graph:

(a) The pressure at 10.0 mL _____

(b) The volume at 700 torr _____

# EXERCISE 10

## Moles

Show calculation setups and answers for all problems.

1. Find the molar mass of (a) nitric acid, $HNO_3$; (b) potassium bicarbonate, $KHCO_3$; and (c) Nickel(II) nitrate, $Ni(NO_3)_2$.

(a) _____

(b) _____

(c) _____

2. A sample of mercury(II) bromide, $HgBr_2$, weighs 87.34 g. How many moles are in this sample?

_____

3. What is the mass of 2.57 mol of ammonium sulfate, $(NH_4)_2SO_4$?

_____

4. How many molecules are contained in 23.54 mol of nitrogen gas, $N_2$?

_____

5. Calculate the percent composition by mass of calcium sulfite, $CaSO_3$.

Ca _____

S _____

O _____

6. An organic compound is analyzed and found to be carbon 51.90%, hydrogen 9.80%, and chlorine 38.30%. What is the empirical formula of this compound?

_____

7. A sample of oxygen gas, $O_2$, weighs 28.4 g. How many molecules of $O_2$ and how many atoms of O are present in this sample?

_____ molecules of $O_2$

_____ atoms of O

8. A mixture of sand and salt is found to be 48 percent NaCl by mass. How many moles of NaCl are in 74 g of this mixture?

_____

9. What is the mass of $2.6 \times 10^{23}$ molecules of ammonia, $NH_3$?

_____

10. A water solution of sulfuric acid has a density of 1.67 g/mL and is 75 percent $H_2SO_4$ by mass. How many moles of $H_2SO_4$ are contained in 400. mL of this solution?

_____

## EXERCISE 11

## Stoichiometry

Show calculation setups and answers for all problems.

1. Use the equation given to solve the following problems:

$$Na_3PO_4 + 3\,AgNO_3 \longrightarrow Ag_3PO_4 + 3\,NaNO_3$$

(a) How many moles of $Na_3PO_4$ would be required to react with 3.0 mol of $AgNO_3$?

_____

(b) How many moles of $NaNO_3$ can be produced from 1.25 mol of $Na_3PO_4$?

_____

(c) How many grams of $Ag_3PO_4$ can be produced from 65.23 g of $Na_3PO_4$?

_____

(d) If you have 9.44 g of $Na_3PO_4$, how many grams of $AgNO_3$ will be needed for complete reaction?

_____

2. Use the equation given to solve the following problems:

$$2\,KMnO_4 + 16\,HCl \longrightarrow 5\,Cl_2 + 2\,KCl + 2\,MnCl_2 + 8\,H_2O$$

(a) How many moles of HCl are required to react with 65.0 g of $KMnO_4$?

_____

(b) How many $Cl_2$ molecules will be produced using 6.52 mol $KMnO_4$?

_____

(c) To produce 35.0 g of $MnCl_2$, what mass of HCl will need to react?

_____

(d) How many moles of water will be produced from 8.0 mol of $KMnO_4$?

_____

# EXERCISE 12

## Solution Concentrations

Show calculation setups and answers for all problems.

1. What will be the percent composition by mass of a solution made by dissolving 65.00 g of barium nitrate, $Ba(NO_3)_2$, in 125.00 g of water?

$Ba(NO_3)_2$ _____

$H_2O$ _____

2. How many moles of potassium hydroxide, KOH, are required to prepare 4.50 L of 0.250 M solution?

_____

3. What will be the molarity of a solution if 6.32 g of sodium hydroxide, NaOH, are dissolved in water to make 150.0 mL of solution?

_____

4. How many milliliters of 5.24 M solution can be prepared by dissolving 5.00 g of NaBr in water?

_____

5. How many milliliters of 12.0 M HCl is needed to prepare 300. mL of 0.250 M HCl solution?

_____

6. A sample of potassium hydrogen oxalate, $KHC_2O_4$, weighing 0.717 g, was dissolved in water and titrated with 23.47 mL of an NaOH solution. Calculate the molarity of the NaOH solution.

_____

7. How many grams of hydrogen chloride are in 50.0 mL of concentrated (12.0 M) HCl solution?

_____

8. Sulfuric acid reacts with sodium hydroxide according to this equation:

$$H_2SO_4 + 2\,NaOH \longrightarrow Na_2SO_4 + 2\,H_2O$$

A 10.00 mL sample of the $H_2SO_4$ solution required 18.71 mL of 0.248 M NaOH for neutralization. Calculate the molarity of the acid.

_____

# APPENDIX 1

## Units of Measurements

### Numerical Value of Prefixes with Units

| Prefix | Symbol | Number | Power of 10 |
|--------|--------|--------|-------------|
| mega | M | 1,000,000 | $1 \times 10^6$ |
| kilo | k | 1,000 | $1 \times 10^3$ |
| hecto | h | 100 | $1 \times 10^2$ |
| deca | da | 10 | $1 \times 10^1$ |
| deci | d | 0.1 | $1 \times 10^{-1}$ |
| centi | c | 0.01 | $1 \times 10^{-2}$ |
| milli | m | 0.001 | $1 \times 10^{-3}$ |
| micro | μ | 0.000001 | $1 \times 10^{-6}$ |
| nano | n | 0.000000001 | $1 \times 10^{-9}$ |

### Conversion of Units

| | | |
|---|---|---|
| 1 m | = | 1000 mm |
| 1 cm | = | 10 mm |
| 2.54 cm | = | 1 in. |
| 453.6 g | = | 1 lb |
| 1 kg | = | 2.2 lb |
| 1 g | = | 1000 mg |
| 1 L | = | 1000 mL |
| 1 mL | = | $1 \text{ cm}^3$ |
| 0.946 L | = | 1 qt |
| 1 cal | = | 4.184 J |
| 1 torr | = | 1 mm Hg |
| 760 torr | = | 1 atm |

### Metric Abbreviations

| | |
|---|---|
| meter | m |
| centimeter | cm |
| millimeter | mm |
| nanometer | nm |
| liter | L |
| milliliter | mL |
| kilogram | kg |
| gram | g |
| milligram | mg |
| mole | mol |

### Temperature Conversion Formulas

$$°C = \frac{(°F - 32)}{1.8}$$

$$°F = 1.8\,°C + 32$$

$$K = °C + 273$$

# APPENDIX 2

## Solubility Table

| | $C_2H_3O_2^-$ | $AsO_4^{3-}$ | $Br^-$ | $CO_3^{2-}$ | $Cl^-$ | $CrO_4^{2-}$ | $OH^-$ | $I^-$ | $NO_3^-$ | $C_2O_4^{2-}$ | $O^{2-}$ | $PO_4^{3-}$ | $SO_4^{2-}$ | $S^{2-}$ | $SO_3^{2-}$ |
|---|---|---|---|---|---|---|---|---|---|---|---|---|---|---|---|
| $Al^{3+}$ | aq | I | aq | – | aq | – | I | aq | aq | – | I | I | aq | d | – |
| $NH_4^+$ | aq | aq | aq | aq | aq | aq | aq | aq | aq | aq | – | aq | aq | aq | aq |
| $Ba^{2+}$ | aq | I | aq | I | aq | I | sl. aq | aq | aq | I | sl. aq | I | I | d | I |
| $Bi^{3+}$ | – | sl. aq | d | I | d | – | I | I | d | I | I | sl. aq | d | I | – |
| $Ca^{2+}$ | aq | I | aq | I | aq | aq | I | aq | aq | I | I | I | I | d | I |
| $Co^{2+}$ | aq | I | aq | I | aq | I | I | aq | aq | I | I | I | aq | I | I |
| $Cu^{2+}$ | aq | I | aq | I | aq | I | I | – | aq | I | I | I | aq | I | – |
| $Fe^{2+}$ | aq | I | aq | sl. aq | aq | – | I | aq | aq | I | I | I | aq | I | sl. aq |
| $Fe^{3+}$ | I | I | aq | I | aq | I | I | – | aq | aq | I | I | aq | I | – |
| $Pb^{2+}$ | aq | I | I | I | I | I | I | I | aq | I | I | I | I | I | I |
| $Mg^{2+}$ | aq | d | aq | I | aq | aq | I | aq | aq | I | I | I | aq | d | sl. aq |
| $Hg_2^{2+}$ | sl. aq | I | I | I | I | sl. aq | – | I | aq | I | I | I | I | I | – |
| $Hg^{2+}$ | aq | I | I | I | aq | sl. aq | I | I | aq | I | I | I | d | I | – |
| $K^+$ | aq | aq | aq | aq | aq | aq | aq | aq | aq | aq | aq | aq | aq | aq | aq |
| $Ag^+$ | sl. aq | I | I | I | I | I | – | I | aq | I | I | I | I | I | I |
| $Na^+$ | aq | aq | aq | aq | aq | aq | aq | aq | aq | aq | aq | aq | aq | aq | aq |
| $Zn^{2+}$ | aq | I | aq | I | aq | I | I | aq | aq | I | I | I | aq | I | I |

Key:  $aq$ = Soluble in water    I = Insoluble in water (less than 1 g/100 g $H_2O$)
      sl. $aq$ = Slightly soluble in water    d = Decomposes in water

# Periodic Table of the Elements

**Group**

Atomic masses are based on carbon-12. Elements marked with have no stable isotopes. The atomic mass given is that of the isotope with the longest known half-life.

Atomic number → 
Symbol →
Name →
Atomic mass →

| 11 |
|----|
| **Na** |
| Sodium |
| 22.99 |

— Current ACS and IUPAC
— Preferred U.S.

**Transition Elements**

| | Noble Gases |
|---|---|
| | 18 8A |

□ Metals  ▨ Metalloids  ░ Nonmetals

**Period**

| Period | 1 1A | 2 2A | 3 3B | 4 4B | 5 5B | 6 6B | 7 7B | 8 | 9 8B | 10 | 11 1B | 12 2B | 13 3A | 14 4A | 15 5A | 16 6A | 17 7A | 18 8A |
|---|---|---|---|---|---|---|---|---|---|---|---|---|---|---|---|---|---|---|
| 1 | 1 **H** Hydrogen 1.008 | | | | | | | | | | | | | | | | | 2 **He** Helium 4.003 |
| 2 | 3 **Li** Lithium 6.941 | 4 **Be** Beryllium 9.012 | | | | | | | | | | | 5 **B** Boron 10.81 | 6 **C** Carbon 12.01 | 7 **N** Nitrogen 14.01 | 8 **O** Oxygen 16.00 | 9 **F** Fluorine 19.00 | 10 **Ne** Neon 20.18 |
| 3 | 11 **Na** Sodium 22.99 | 12 **Mg** Magnesium 24.31 | | | | | | | | | | | 13 **Al** Aluminum 26.98 | 14 **Si** Silicon 28.09 | 15 **P** Phosphorus 30.97 | 16 **S** Sulfur 32.07 | 17 **Cl** Chlorine 35.45 | 18 **Ar** Argon 39.95 |
| 4 | 19 **K** Potassium 39.10 | 20 **Ca** Calcium 40.08 | 21 **Sc** Scandium 44.96 | 22 **Ti** Titanium 47.87 | 23 **V** Vanadium 50.94 | 24 **Cr** Chromium 52.00 | 25 **Mn** Manganese 54.94 | 26 **Fe** Iron 55.85 | 27 **Co** Cobalt 58.93 | 28 **Ni** Nickel 58.69 | 29 **Cu** Copper 63.55 | 30 **Zn** Zinc 65.39 | 31 **Ga** Gallium 69.72 | 32 **Ge** Germanium 72.61 | 33 **As** Arsenic 74.92 | 34 **Se** Selenium 78.96 | 35 **Br** Bromine 79.90 | 36 **Kr** Krypton 83.80 |
| 5 | 37 **Rb** Rubidium 85.47 | 38 **Sr** Strontium 87.62 | 39 **Y** Yttrium 88.91 | 40 **Zr** Zirconium 91.22 | 41 **Nb** Niobium 92.91 | 42 **Mo** Molybdenum 95.94 | 43 **Tc** Technetium 97.91 | 44 **Ru** Ruthenium 101.1 | 45 **Rh** Rhodium 102.9 | 46 **Pd** Palladium 106.4 | 47 **Ag** Silver 107.9 | 48 **Cd** Cadmium 112.4 | 49 **In** Indium 114.8 | 50 **Sn** Tin 118.7 | 51 **Sb** Antimony 121.8 | 52 **Te** Tellurium 127.6 | 53 **I** Iodine 126.9 | 54 **Xe** Xenon 131.3 |
| 6 | 55 **Cs** Cesium 132.9 | 56 **Ba** Barium 137.3 | 57 **La** Lanthanum 138.9 * | 72 **Hf** Hafnium 178.5 | 73 **Ta** Tantalum 180.9 | 74 **W** Tungsten 183.8 | 75 **Re** Rhenium 186.2 | 76 **Os** Osmium 190.2 | 77 **Ir** Iridium 192.2 | 78 **Pt** Platinum 195.1 | 79 **Au** Gold 197.0 | 80 **Hg** Mercury 200.6 | 81 **Tl** Thallium 204.4 | 82 **Pb** Lead 207.2 | 83 **Bi** Bismuth 209.0 | 84 **Po** Polonium 209.0 | 85 **At** Astatine 210.0 | 86 **Rn** Radon 222.0 |
| 7 | 87 **Fr** Francium 223.0 | 88 **Ra** Radium 226.0 | 89 **Ac** Actinium 227.0 ** | 104 **Rf** Rutherfordium 261.1 | 105 **Db** Dubnium — | 106 **Sg** Seaborgium — | 107 **Bh** Bohrium — | 108 **Hs** Hassium — | 109 **Mt** Meitnerium — | 110 **Ds** Darmstadtium — | 111 **Rg** Roentgenium — | | | | | | | |

# Inner Transition Elements

**Lanthanide Series** *
6

| 58 **Ce** Cerium 140.1 | 59 **Pr** Praseodymium 140.9 | 60 **Nd** Neodymium 144.2 | 61 **Pm** Promethium 144.9 | 62 **Sm** Samarium 150.4 | 63 **Eu** Europium 152.0 | 64 **Gd** Gadolinium 157.3 | 65 **Tb** Terbium 158.9 | 66 **Dy** Dysprosium 162.5 | 67 **Ho** Holmium 164.9 | 68 **Er** Erbium 167.3 | 69 **Tm** Thulium 168.9 | 70 **Yb** Ytterbium 173.0 | 71 **Lu** Lutetium 175.0 |
|---|---|---|---|---|---|---|---|---|---|---|---|---|---|

**Actinide Series** **
7

| 90 **Th** Thorium 232.0 | 91 **Pa** Protactinium 231.0 | 92 **U** Uranium 238.0 | 93 **Np** Neptunium 237.0 | 94 **Pu** Plutonium 244.1 | 95 **Am** Americium 243.1 | 96 **Cm** Curium 247.1 | 97 **Bk** Berkelium 247.1 | 98 **Cf** Californium 251.1 | 99 **Es** Einsteinium 252.1 | 100 **Fm** Fermium 257.1 | 101 **Md** Mendelevium 258.1 | 102 **No** Nobelium 259.1 | 103 **Lr** Lawrencium 262.1 |
|---|---|---|---|---|---|---|---|---|---|---|---|---|---|

## Atomic Masses of the Elements
### Based on the IUPAC Table of Atomic Masses

| Name | Symbol | Atomic Number | Atomic Mass | Name | Symbol | Atomic Number | Atomic Mass |
|---|---|---|---|---|---|---|---|
| Actinium* | Ac | 89 | 227.0277 | Meitnerium | Mt | 109 | — |
| Aluminum | Al | 13 | 26.981538 | Mendelevium* | Md | 101 | 258.0984 |
| Americium* | Am | 95 | 243.0614 | Mercury | Hg | 80 | 200.59 |
| Antimony | Sb | 51 | 121.760 | Molybdenum | Mo | 42 | 95.94 |
| Argon | Ar | 18 | 39.948 | Neodymium | Nd | 60 | 144.24 |
| Arsenic | As | 33 | 74.92160 | Neon | Ne | 10 | 20.1797 |
| Astatine* | At | 85 | 209.9871 | Neptunium* | Np | 93 | 237.0482 |
| Barium | Ba | 56 | 137.327 | Nickel | Ni | 28 | 58.6934 |
| Berkelium* | Bk | 97 | 247.0703 | Niobium | Nb | 41 | 92.90638 |
| Beryllium | Be | 4 | 9.012182 | Nitrogen | N | 7 | 14.00674 |
| Bismuth | Bi | 83 | 208.98038 | Nobelium* | No | 102 | 259.1011 |
| Bohrium | Bh | 107 | — | Osmium | Os | 76 | 190.23 |
| Boron | B | 5 | 10.811 | Oxygen | O | 8 | 15.9994 |
| Bromine | Br | 35 | 79.904 | Palladium | Pd | 46 | 106.42 |
| Cadmium | Cd | 48 | 112.411 | Phosphorus | P | 15 | 30.973762 |
| Calcium | Ca | 20 | 40.078 | Platinum | Pt | 78 | 195.078 |
| Californium* | Cf | 98 | 251.0796 | Plutonium* | Pu | 94 | 244.0642 |
| Carbon | C | 6 | 12.0107 | Polonium* | Po | 84 | 208.9824 |
| Cerium | Ce | 58 | 140.116 | Potassium | K | 19 | 39.0983 |
| Cesium | Cs | 55 | 132.90545 | Praseodymium | Pr | 59 | 140.90765 |
| Chlorine | Cl | 17 | 35.4527 | Promethium* | Pm | 61 | 144.9127 |
| Chromium | Cr | 24 | 51.9961 | Protactinium* | Pa | 91 | 231.03588 |
| Cobalt | Co | 27 | 58.933200 | Radium* | Ra | 88 | 226.0254 |
| Copper | Cu | 29 | 63.546 | Radon* | Rn | 86 | 222.0176 |
| Curium* | Cm | 96 | 247.0703 | Rhenium | Re | 75 | 186.207 |
| Darmstadtium | Ds | 110 | — | Rhodium | Rh | 45 | 102.90550 |
| Dubnium | Db | 105 | — | Rubidium | Rb | 37 | 85.4678 |
| Dysprosium | Dy | 66 | 162.50 | Ruthenium | Ru | 44 | 101.07 |
| Einsteinium* | Es | 99 | 252.0830 | Rutherfordium | Rf | 104 | 261.1089 |
| Erbium | Er | 68 | 167.26 | Samarium | Sm | 62 | 150.36 |
| Europium | Eu | 63 | 151.964 | Scandium | Sc | 21 | 44.955910 |
| Fermium* | Fm | 100 | 257.0951 | Seaborgium | Sg | 106 | — |
| Fluorine | F | 9 | 18.9984032 | Selenium | Se | 34 | 78.96 |
| Francium* | Fr | 87 | 233.0197 | Silicon | Si | 14 | 28.0855 |
| Gadolinium | Gd | 64 | 157.25 | Silver | Ag | 47 | 107.8682 |
| Gallium | Ga | 31 | 69.723 | Sodium | Na | 11 | 22.989770 |
| Germanium | Ge | 32 | 72.61 | Strontium | Sr | 38 | 87.62 |
| Gold | Au | 79 | 196.96655 | Sulfur | S | 16 | 32.066 |
| Hafnium | Hf | 72 | 178.49 | Tantalum | Ta | 73 | 180.9479 |
| Hassium | Hs | 108 | — | Technetium* | Tc | 43 | 97.9072 |
| Helium | He | 2 | 4.002602 | Tellurium | Te | 52 | 127.60 |
| Holmium | Ho | 67 | 164.93032 | Terbium | Tb | 65 | 158.92534 |
| Hydrogen | H | 1 | 1.00794 | Thallium | Tl | 81 | 204.3833 |
| Indium | In | 49 | 114.818 | Thorium* | Th | 90 | 232.0381 |
| Iodine | I | 53 | 126.90447 | Thulium | Tm | 69 | 168.93421 |
| Iridium | Ir | 77 | 192.217 | Tin | Sn | 50 | 118.710 |
| Iron | Fe | 26 | 55.845 | Titanium | Ti | 22 | 47.867 |
| Krypton | Kr | 36 | 83.80 | Tungsten | W | 74 | 183.84 |
| Lanthanum | La | 57 | 138.9055 | Uranium* | U | 92 | 238.0289 |
| Lawrencium* | Lr | 103 | 262.110 | Vanadium | V | 23 | 50.9415 |
| Lead | Pb | 82 | 207.2 | Xenon | Xe | 54 | 131.29 |
| Lithium | Li | 3 | 6.941 | Ytterbium | Yb | 70 | 173.04 |
| Lutetium | Lu | 71 | 174.967 | Yttrium | Y | 39 | 88.90585 |
| Magnesium | Mg | 12 | 24.3050 | Zinc | Zn | 30 | 65.39 |
| Manganese | Mn | 25 | 54.938049 | Zirconium | Zr | 40 | 91.224 |

*This element has no stable isotopes. The atomic mass given is that of the isotope with the longest known half-life.

# NAMES, FORMULAS AND CHARGES OF COMMON IONS

| | Positive Ions (Cations) | | Negative Ions (Anions) | |
|---|---|---|---|---|
| **1+** | Ammonium | $NH_4^+$ | Acetate | $C_2H_3O_2^-$ |
| | Copper(I) | $Cu^+$ | Bromate | $BrO_3^-$ |
| | (Cuprous) | | Bromide | $Br^-$ |
| | Hydrogen | $H^+$ | Chlorate | $ClO_3^-$ |
| | Potassium | $K^+$ | Chloride | $Cl^-$ |
| | Silver | $Ag^+$ | Chlorite | $ClO_2^-$ |
| | Sodium | $Na^+$ | Cyanide | $CN^-$ |
| **2+** | Barium | $Ba^{2+}$ | Fluoride | $F^-$ |
| | Cadmium | $Cd^{2+}$ | Hydride | $H^-$ |
| | Calcium | $Ca^{2+}$ | Hydrogen carbonate | $HCO_3^-$ |
| | Cobalt(II) | $Co^{2+}$ | (Bicarbonate) | |
| | Copper(II) | $Cu^{2+}$ | Hydrogen sulfate | $HSO_4^-$ |
| | (Cupric) | | (Bisulfate) | |
| | Iron(II) | $Fe^{2+}$ | Hydrogen sulfite | $HSO_3^-$ |
| | (Ferrous) | | (Bisulfite) | |
| | Lead(II) | $Pb^{2+}$ | Hydroxide | $OH^-$ |
| | Magnesium | $Mg^{2+}$ | Hypochlorite | $ClO^-$ |
| | Manganese(II) | $Mn^{2+}$ | Iodate | $IO_3^-$ |
| | Mercury(II) | $Hg^{2+}$ | Iodide | $I^-$ |
| | (Mercuric) | | Nitrate | $NO_3^-$ |
| | Nickel(II) | $Ni^{2+}$ | Nitrite | $NO_2^-$ |
| | Tin(II) | $Sn^{2+}$ | Perchlorate | $ClO_4^-$ |
| | (Stannous) | | Permanganate | $MnO_4^-$ |
| | Zinc | $Zn^{2+}$ | Thiocyanate | $SCN^-$ |
| **3+** | Aluminum | $Al^{3+}$ | Carbonate | $CO_3^{2-}$ |
| | Antimony(III) | $Sb^{3+}$ | Chromate | $CrO_4^{2-}$ |
| | Arsenic(III) | $As^{3+}$ | Dichromate | $Cr_2O_7^{2-}$ |
| | Bismuth(III) | $Bi^{3+}$ | Oxalate | $C_2O_4^{2-}$ |
| | Chromium(III) | $Cr^{3+}$ | Oxide | $O^{2-}$ |
| | Iron(III) | $Fe^{3+}$ | Peroxide | $O_2^{2-}$ |
| | (Ferric) | | Silicate | $SiO_3^{2-}$ |
| | Titanium(III) | $Ti^{3+}$ | Sulfate | $SO_4^{2-}$ |
| | (Titanous) | | Sulfide | $S^{2-}$ |
| **4+** | Manganese(IV) | $Mn^{4+}$ | Sulfite | $SO_3^{2-}$ |
| | Tin(IV) | $Sn^{4+}$ | Arsenate | $AsO_4^{3-}$ |
| | (Stannic) | | Borate | $BO_3^{3-}$ |
| | Titanium(IV) | $Ti^{4+}$ | Phosphate | $PO_4^{3-}$ |
| | (Titanic) | | Phosphide | $P^{3-}$ |
| **5+** | Antimony(V) | $Sb^{5+}$ | Phosphite | $PO_3^{3-}$ |
| | Arsenic(V) | $As^{5+}$ | | |

The anion charge groups are labeled **1-**, **2-**, and **3-** in the right-hand column.

Graph paper with 10mm. grid

Graph paper with 10mm. grid

Graph paper with 10mm. grid

Graph paper with 10mm. grid